STO

Young Jed Smith

Westering Boy

BY

OLIVE W. BURT

ILLUSTRATED BY

Harry Lees

THE BOBBS-MERRILL COMPANY, INC.

Publishers

INDIANAPOLIS   NEW YORK

To
Barbara Jean
A grandniece is just *grand!*

CONTENTS

LIST OF FULL-PAGE ILLUSTRATIONS

YOUNG JED SMITH

Westering Boy

I

A BIG BROWN BEAR

"YES SIREE! It's the biggest feller I ever did see! Must weigh more 'n fifty stone!"

"More 'n seven hundred pounds! That's a mighty big bear!"

Jed Smith stopped whittling and listened.

"Got him strung up on the trees in front of his cabin, Dan'l has, so 's everybody kin see him."

Jed slipped down from his perch on the stack of hides. He went across the room to the group of men. They were standing at the long counter in the Smiths' trading post near Jericho, down toward the southern border of New York State. Past the post door flowed the Susquehanna River. The river was the highway that brought the men to the trading post. They were roughly dressed men with heavy, long beards. This was

13

the spring of 1808, and these were frontiersmen, every one of them.

Jed's bare feet made no sound on the rough wooden floor, but the men wouldn't have noticed him, anyway.

"I tell ye, Smith," Neighbor Wright was saying to Jed's father, "ye ought to go over an' see him. He sure is a fine specimen."

Jed nudged young Matt Cooper. "What critter are they talking about?"

Matt had been listening to the men ever since they had come into the post. Before that he had been playing with Jed. But Matt liked gossip. "Old Dan'l Elliott," he whispered back, "killed a bear right in these-here woods! A big brown bear!"

Jed's father leaned on the counter. He spoke in a slow, comfortable drawl through his heavy beard. "I'd like to see that bear, Nathan," he agreed. "But I can't see my way clear to leave right now."

"Ah, Pa! Let's go!" Jed begged.

His father grinned down at him. "Like I say, son, I'd sure enough like to go. But I can't." He turned to Nathan Wright again. "My older boy, Ralph, is down to Binghamton. My wife and the girls have gone over to Mis' Cooper's to a quilting. I'm the only one here."

Jed looked up into his father's kind gray eyes. He knew that when *that* Jed Smith said a thing, he meant it. Matt shrugged and started out of the door. Jed followed his friend. *"I* can go!" he said to Matt. "I'm going. I aim to see that bear."

Matt stared at Jed. The two boys were the same age, nine years old. Jed was slim and tall for his age. He had an air of confidence about him. Matt was much shorter and more timid.

It was Jed who decided things when they played together.

"It's a far piece." Matt hesitated.

"Three miles by the road," Jed answered. He knew all the roads thereabouts. He had visited every cabin in these woods along the banks of the Susquehanna. He always went along with his father and older brother when they made trips to the neighbors'.

Matt shook his head. "That's a far piece," he said again.

"We can go by the old Mohawk Trail," Jed suggested eagerly. "Not even two miles that way."

Without any more argument Jed started toward the wagon track that led into the forest. He knew that the old Indian trail branched off from this track.

Matt watched his friend. He wanted to go too.

He wanted to see that bear just as much as Jed did. But he was a stay-at-home boy.

Jed looked over his shoulder. "Coming, Matt?" he asked.

"Are you really going?" Matt didn't need to wait for an answer. Jed's bare feet were moving fast. Matt gave one glance at the friendly trading post. Then he followed his comrade at a dogtrot. His short legs had to work fast to catch up with the taller boy.

When he was close enough to talk, he asked, panting a little, "Do you know the way, sure, Jed?"

"Course I do. I've been to the Elliotts' lots of times. Just follow the trail."

Trotting along, Matt looked up at the trees. They were tall and close together, crowding the wagon tracks.

Jed, still ahead of his companion, came to the

place where the trail broke away from the two ruts of the wagon road.

"Here it is, Matt!" he yelled excitedly. "See!" He pointed to the ground. There, plain to be seen, was the Indian trail. It was a narrow path, just about a foot wide, worn deep into the ground. Jed stepped into it. He wiggled his bare toes in the dirt.

"I get plumb excited every time I set foot in this old trail!" he said. "Look how deep it is. I bet Indians traipsed over this-here trail for a hundred years!"

Matt came up and stood looking at the narrow path. His eyes followed it to where it disappeared among tall elms and maples and spreading oaks.

"I've been over the road with Pa," he said doubtfully. "But I've never been on this trail. You sure it's the right one?"

Jed looked at his friend. What was Matt

scared of? An Indian trail was just as good as any old wagon road. Better because it was shorter. Indians could go almost straight from place to place, traveling on foot as they did.

"Come on," Jed encouraged. He began to move, sure-footed along the trail.

Matt followed. He kept looking to right and left. He wished he could see what was behind every tree trunk. He wished Jed would talk to him. Jed wasn't much of a one to gabble. But the sound of a voice would make things a lot more cheerful here in the dark shadows.

"Jed?"

"Huh?"

"What part of the woods did Dan'l Elliott kill the bear in? Was it around here somewheres?"

"I don't know. You were the one listening to all the talk."

The two boys went on. The trees grew still closer together. It was gloomy here. You couldn't see even a speck of sky. They didn't talk. Jed had nothing to say and Matt couldn't think of anything.

Then suddenly the stillness was broken. Somewhere, not very close and yet not far away, something moved in the forest. A twig snapped.

Matt's legs carried him close to Jed. He grabbed his friend's hickory shirttail. The coarse, striped cloth gave him a little reassurance. "What's that?"

Jed had stopped. He looked around. Matt had reason to be scared now. Something was coming toward them. It crashed along the Indian trail over which they had just passed. The noise grew more fearful as it came closer.

"Jed!" Matt was close to tears.

"Aw!" Jed's eyes were studying the trees. They were too high to climb. There was no way to escape. "Don't be scared, Matt!" His own voice shook a little.

"A bear!" Matt squeaked. He cowered against his companion.

"Wish I had my bow 'n arrows!" Jed muttered.

Just then a large, brown furry form leaped out of the brush beside them. It came straight for Jed. Matt gave a shrill yelp of terror and flung his hands up over his face.

Jed began to laugh. "Hey, Wampum, old boy! Look, Matt, it's Wampum! It's just Ralph's dog. Came to keep us company."

Matt uncovered his eyes. He saw the big brown dog licking Jed's face. He advanced shakily. "Hi!" he said bravely. Then he said to Jed in a weak voice, "He made as much noise as a grizzly bear."

"Come along, Wampum!" Jed invited. He turned to explain over his shoulder, "Ralph is down at Binghamton. Old Wampum must've been lonesome."

"I'm glad he came," Matt said.

A little later the boys came to a fork in the trail. One path led off to the northwest, the other to the southwest. Jed stopped. Matt came up and halted, too.

"Which one, Jed?" he asked anxiously.

Jed thought. There was a frown between his gray eyes. Then he said, "This one," and started along the northern path.

Matt hung back. "Jed," he began, "if this is the wrong one, we'll get lost."

But Jed walked on. He was sure he was right. Still farther along, the trail forked again. This time Jed unhesitatingly took the lower fork.

Matt had given up trying to get his companion to talk. He trotted along in Jed's footsteps, saying nothing. He just wished they'd come to the Elliotts' cabin. Finally he could stand the silence no longer. He blurted out, "Jed, why don't you talk? You're the un-talkingest boy I ever knew.

Back there in your pa's trading post you just sat and whittled. Why don't you talk?"

"I talk," Jed answered. "I talk when I have something to say."

At last they came out of the trees into a clearing. Jed grinned. There was the Elliotts' cabin. He began to run across the clearing. Wampum, barking and making a fearful racket, dashed past him.

Jed chuckled. He knew what was exciting the dog. It was the bear—the big brown bear. It hung from a stout pole suspended between two tall trees just outside the cabin.

The boys dashed across the ground toward the bear. Wampum was already leaping up at the great animal's body. He barked wildly.

The door of the cabin opened and a bearded man stepped out. In his hand was a flintlock musket. He yelled at Wampum, and then he saw Jed and Matt. A smile curved his bearded lips. "Hullo thar! You boys come over to see my catch?"

"Yes, sir!" Jed answered. "Golly whackers, he's a big fellow!"

"Pretty nigh everybody in Chenango County's been to see him," Mr. Elliott said. "Come a mite closer and look him over. See those claws!"

Jed stepped close. He put out a hand and touched the bear's huge paw. The long, sharp claws looked frightful. "One swipe of that paw could do for a man, I reckon," he said soberly.

"It sure could," Dan'l Elliott agreed. He took his musket back into the cabin.

Dan'l's wife, Hester, came out. She was surprised to see the two boys alone, without their fathers. "Why, Jed Smith! What are you doing away over here?" she scolded good-naturedly. "And little Matt Cooper! Gracious, did you come all the way from the post just to see that critter? I declare to goodness, you'd think folks

Jed touched the bear's huge paw.

25

around here had never seen a brown bear before!"

"I reckon they haven't—not one so big as that!" Jed answered.

"Well, you boys must be hungry! Here, sit down on that log and rest. I'll bring you a slice of bread and honey and a mug of milk."

Jed and Matt sat down obediently. They weren't tired but they were hungry. Just as soon as Mrs. Elliott went into the cabin, Jed was on his feet again. He couldn't leave that bear alone. There was a lot to see.

The animal's jaws hung open. His yellow teeth made Jed shudder. The small, cruel eyes stared at the boy from the brushy, short hairs around them. The front legs, short and powerful, could easily crush a man to death.

"I can't look at him!" Matt shuddered.

"He'd sure be a bad critter to meet in the woods!" Jed admitted.

Mrs. Elliott came back from the cabin. She brought two gray earthen mugs of milk and two thick wedges of bread smeared with yellow honey.

Jed sat down beside Matt and took the food with a grin. "Honey!" he exclaimed, smacking his lips. "Mr. Elliott must've found a bee tree."

"That he did." Mrs. Elliott chuckled. "That old bear had found it, too. That's how Dan'l met up with him. But," she added soberly, "I'm mighty thankful Dan'l's a good shot!"

Jed sank his teeth into the good bread and honey.

Mrs. Elliott went on: "You tell your folks we're going to have a bear roast here on Saturday. Everybody's to come—everybody! Don't you forget!"

"I won't," Jed promised. How could he forget to tell about a bear roast? And wasn't it lucky he had come? Now he would have the chance to spread the good news about the feast.

The boys finished their lunch. They gave the mugs back to Mrs. Elliott. They took another good look at the bear. Then, with Wampum frisking about their heels, they started for home.

They had no trouble going back. They played along, not hurrying too fast. Now that they had seen that big bear hanging helpless from the pole, they were less afraid of meeting one in the woods.

"If bears have any sense at all," Jed observed, "they'll skedaddle right away from these parts. If they don't, old Dan'l will get them for sure."

They were nearly home when Jed, who was still ahead of his companion, stopped dead in his tracks. He listened. The sound came again: "Jed! Jedediah!"

Jed put his hands to his mouth, making a

trumpet of them. "Hello!" he yelled. "I'm coming!"

He said over his shoulder, "That's Eunice. Soon's she doesn't know where I am, she starts hollering."

As the boys came out of the trees they saw Jed's ten-year-old sister. She was waiting for them. She was very cross. "Jed," she scolded, "where've you been? I've been calling and calling. Ma was just about to set out to find you, but Pa allowed you'd probably gone over to the Elliotts' to see that bear!" She broke into a wail. "Why didn't you take me along?"

"I didn't think to," Jed answered. "I just got to thinking about that bear."

"I know," Eunice grumbled. "Once you think of going some place, you just up and go. You never think of me!" Her lips puckered. "I wanted to see it, too!"

"What does Ma want me for, anyhow?" Jed asked.

"Dr. Simons has come."

"Dr. Simons! Whoopee! Did Sol come too?" Jed shouted. He started to run toward the trading post. Solomon Simons, the doctor's son, was older than Jed. Jed looked up to him as a hero.

Eunice caught him by the shirttail. "Don't

Eunice caught Jed by the shirttail.

you go roaring in like that! He didn't bring his family along. They're living in a log cabin in Erie, Pennsylvania. He's talking business with Pa."

Jed stopped tugging to get away. "What sort of business?" he asked.

"He wants Pa to sell the trading post and go to Erie."

"Go to Pennsylvania!" Jed exclaimed. "When Dr. Simons moved away he promised he'd come back. He said he'd find out what it was like out west there. Then he'd come back and get us. He even said he'd be my teacher again when he didn't have to be doctoring. Golly whackers! Let go of me. I got to go in and see about this."

He gave a quick jerk. His shirttail slipped out of Eunice's hand. He dashed onto the wide porch and through the trading-post door. Matt looked after him and then slowly trudged on toward his own home, half a mile down the river.

II

GOOD-BY TO JERICHO

1. *The Great News*

JED was bursting with excitement. It wasn't only the bear roast, though that was enough to make anyone excited. It was the news—the great news he had to tell.

A wagon, loaded with the whole Smith family, bumped over the rutted forest road. Jed knew they were all there, but he counted them over to be sure. There were Pa and Ma. Then Sally and Betsey, young ladies of sixteen and twelve, as tall as Ma in their calico dresses and ruffled sunbonnets. Then Ralph, putting on airs because he was thirteen. And Eunice. "And me!" Jed whispered, grinning to himself. "And Dr. Simons."

As Jed looked at his friend and teacher he

thought, "Too bad Dr. Simons had to leave his family back in Pennsylvania! Ma'd like to have Mrs. Simons here—and wouldn't Louisa and Sol love a hunk of that bear meat?"

As the wagon pulled into the clearing around the Elliotts' cabin, Jed thought the whole of Chenango County must be there.

Tall, bearded men in homespun clothing were gathered in little groups "chawin' the rag." Women were bustling around the open fires. Already the huge chunks of bear meat were sizzling. Jed sniffed the smell of hot, fat meat. It made his mouth water. Children were chasing one another among the trees, or playing mumblety-peg on the short grass.

When Matt saw the Smith wagon he came running. "Jed! Jed!" he yelled. "You're not moving away, are you?"

Jed put one bare foot on the slowly turning back wheel of the wagon. He leaped nimbly to the ground. "Yep, we are!" he shouted. He wanted everyone to hear. "We're moving west!"

The men stopped talking and turned to look at the Smiths. Then they came forward crowding around the wagon. "What's this, Jed?" they asked Mr. Smith.

The children stopped playing and made a little knot around young Jed. They were curious and excited. It was a big event when anyone left the Susquehanna Valley to go west.

"What you going for?" Matt asked peevishly. "I wouldn't go if I were you. Whyn't you stay here?"

"I want to go!" Jed answered. "I want to see what's out there. Dr. Simons says——"

"It's that old Simons! Just 'cause he used to be your teacher! Just 'cause he said you're smart with book larnin'!" Matt grumbled. "He moves away and now he comes back to take you, too. You know what?"

Jed looked at his friend.

Matt said, "He just wants to have you where he can make you study books, that's what!"

Jed's brother Ralph was standing near. When Matt said this, Ralph laughed. "You're plumb right, Matt!" he crowed. "That's what the doctor wants. He even said so."

"But I want to study books——" Jed began.

"I don't!" Ralph said stoutly. "I don't see much sense in old books. I'd rather study the woods and the animals."

"I'll study those, too!" Jed put in resolutely.

"You think you will!" Ralph scoffed. "But when you get your nose stuck in a book, you'll forget all the wood larnin' you have."

The corners of Matt's mouth drew down. "Yes, you will, Jed!"

Jed shook his head. How could he forget all the wood learning he had? How could he forget the feel of Indian trails under his bare feet? The

way to tell directions by the moss on tree trunks?
How to read the signs of animals' tracks?

Someone else had joined the group of boys.
Dr. Simons laid his hand on Jed's tousled head.
"Don't worry, Jed," he said kindly. "I would
not take one whit of your nature lore from you."

"Hi there, you younkers!" Dan'l Elliott
yelled. "We need wood and water. Better stop
that palavering and get those legs a-moving."

The group broke up. The boys went off in
little clusters to fetch wood and water. But as
they worked they jabbered about the Smiths.

Jed, doing his share, heard snatches of the
talk. He heard Hester Elliott say to his mother,
"How do you feel, Sary, about this move?"

Mrs. Smith sighed. "I don't know, Hester.
If Jed thinks it best, that's all that really counts.
And Titus Simons says there'll be far more
chance to get ahead out there."

Hester nodded slowly. "That's what the men always say."

Jed's mother went on: "The trading post did well for a while. But it's not doing much now. Folks go down to Binghamton now there's a road."

"And that new road from Albany won't go past here, Dan'l says. That will sort of leave your post stranded, I reckon."

"We've got to think of the children," Jed's mother said firmly.

Yes, Jed knew that was why his parents were moving from York State. They wanted to give the children a chance to get ahead. But he wanted some other things, too. He wanted to see other parts of the country. They had been here long enough.

Jed said to Matt, who had tagged along with him, "I don't see why folks ever settle down. My grandpappy didn't. My grandpappy was one of the first white men that ever came out to this part of York State. But, shucks, he didn't stay! Ma says you couldn't hold Jabin Strong to any one place. He was her pa. He went all over the West. And do you know what?"

Matt nodded. Of course he knew. Jed had told him this story a hundred times. But Matt wouldn't say anything. When Jed had a notion to talk, he would listen.

Jed went on excitedly. He always got excited when he thought of his grandfather's great adventure. "You know what? He was in a boat going down the Niagara River and he came to that place where there are great big falls. Biggest falls in the whole world, I bet. And my grandfather went right spang over those falls in his boat. He thought he was sure going to die right there. But he didn't. He lived all right. And he went back to old Vermont and told everyone about the country out here."

Matt listened patiently, though he knew the story by heart.

"My pa heard him talk about it, long before Pa and Ma got married. So they came out here."

"Then why's he moving away," Matt asked, "if your grandpappy thought this was such good country?"

"Because my pa has fiddle-feet. His feet are always itching to dance to a faraway tune. That's what Ma says. I've got 'em, too!" Jed added proudly.

"Fiddle-feet!" Matt chanted. He was angry that his best friend was going away. Who would play with him now? "Fiddle-feet!" he yelled again.

Jed grinned. Matt would have to think of something else to make him angry.

They brought their armful of dry wood back to the fire and stood listening to the men talk. All the conversation was about the Smiths' leav-

ing. The bear roast had turned into a farewell
party.

Matt tugged at Jed's sleeve. "Jed! When you
going to start?"

"Monday!" Jed answered. "Day after tomorrow."

Matt's eyes filled with tears he couldn't hold
back.

Jed went on: "Look, Matt. I'm not going to
take Stripy, my pet skunk. You come over Monday morning and I'll give him to you."

2. *Off for Pennsylvania!*

Jed was up early Monday morning, stuffing
his things into the canvas plunder bag his mother
had made for him to carry his belongings. Standing on the floor, the bag reached past his knees.
It ought to hold everything. He was just trying

to get his real Mohawk moccasins into the crammed bag when Matt came.

The smaller boy stood watching his friend. "You going to take those mocs?" he asked.

Jed was stuffing his things into the plunder bag.

"If I can get them into my plunder bag," Jed answered. He pushed and tugged to make room.

"Why're you taking them?" Matt persisted. "You know they're too tight. And your feet are getting bigger every day."

Jed looked down at his bare feet. He wiggled his big toe. "Yep!" he agreed. "But these are genuine Mohawk moccasins. Old Chief Porcupine Quill from upriver traded them to Pa for some sugar." He was still trying to push the moccasins into the bag.

Just then his mother came into the room. She stared at Jed. "Why, Jedediah Smith!" she said, half laughing and half scolding. "What on earth! Look there! All your clothing is on your cot—but your bag is full. What have you put into it?"

Jed glanced from the crammed bag to the stack of clothing. "Oh, Ma," he said, "I won't ever need all those things! And I do need these!"

"You'll need what little clothing you have, son. Goodness knows, it isn't much. One extra shirt, your knit hose——"

"I can go barefoot."

"Not in winter, Jed!" His mother pulled

open the plunder bag and looked inside. "You can't take all this stuff. There just won't be room. You'll have to leave most of these things. Now hurry up, or we'll be leaving without you. Empty that bag and put in your clothing."

She bustled out of the room. She had a great deal to do that morning.

Reluctantly Jed held the moccasins out to Matt. "Here," he said, "you can have them."

Matt grabbed them eagerly and immediately slipped his own bare feet into them. "See!" he cried happily. "They just fit me!"

Jed began pulling things out of his bag. "I've just got to take this bow and these arrows," he muttered. He laid the Indian bow and arrows on top of the little pile of clothing. "And this bear trap."

"That's pretty big," Matt pointed out.

Jed looked at the trap. He had made it himself. He had hoped to catch a bear in it.

"Why don't you leave it here?" Matt suggested. "I'll set it for you. If I catch a bear, it'll be half yours."

"I guess I'll never see the bear," Jed grumbled, "but you can have the trap."

Matt put the clumsy wooden contraption on the floor beside him.

Next Jed pulled from his bag an ugly old fox-skin with all the hair worn off. He had found it in the woods one day and brought it home. And there were some bones of animals—he didn't know what kind. And some pine cones and bark. Jed shut his eyes and gritted his teeth. He threw all his treasures out onto the floor. As each one fell Matt asked, "Can I have it?" and Jed nodded.

At last he came to the bottom of the bag. Now, without stopping to think about it, he crammed in his clothing and the bow and arrows. He could hardly get these in.

"Jedediah," his mother was calling, "come eat your breakfast! We must hurry."

The family ate in silence. They all seemed rather sad now that the time for leaving had come. Only Dr. Simons and Jed were cheerful. They looked at each other and winked.

Mr. and Mrs. Crowfoot from upriver had bought the post. They were camped outside, waiting for the Smiths to leave. Every time Jed's mother looked at them through the window, she turned away quickly.

After breakfast Dr. Simons said happily, "The boat's waiting, folks. Get your gear and we'll be off!"

Jed jumped up excitedly. He, for one, was ready. He had helped pack the boat last night. Everything had been put in except their beds and cook things. And his plunder bag. Their big wagon had been taken apart and stowed on board. The horses had been sold to the Crowfoots. They'd buy a new team in Pennsylvania. And this morning, while Jed had been busy packing his gear, the others had been at work, too. Everything was ready....

Jed's mother looked around the room where they had lived for so many years. Tears came to her eyes. Jed went over and touched his mother's arm. "Come on, Ma!" he begged. "Don't you mind leaving. New places are fun. You'll see!"

His mother wiped the tears from her eyes. She smiled at her younger son. "Come, then," she said. "Get your bag, Jed. We're on our way!"

"On our way! On our way!" sang Jed. He threw his plunder bag across his shoulder and marched out of the store. Down across the grassy clearing he went to the little wooden dock. There the heavy flatboat waited. Matt appeared from nowhere and trotted along beside him.

Matt had nothing to say now. Jed had been

his best friend. Now he knew he would probably never see him again.

But Jed was happy. His heart was thumping with excitement. "Here I be, Dr. Simons!" he yelled. He threw his bag onto the boat. "Here I be, ready to sail!"

Dr. Simons held out his hand to help Jed aboard. But the boy needed no help. He gave a jump, and landed among the bundles and boxes.

"Better settle down or you'll tip us over!" Dr. Simons said jokingly. "How'd you like to see all this gear going to the bottom of the Susquehanna, eh?"

Jed found a place on a pile of bedding. Sally and Betsey and Eunice came slowly across the clearing. They turned at every step to look back. Dr. Simons helped them into the boat.

Then Jed's mother came. She didn't look back. She, too, was helped into the boat and found a place to sit. She kept her eyes ahead, watching the river.

Last of all came Jed's father and Ralph with Wampum dancing at their heels. They were loaded with last-minute things. They climbed aboard and stowed away their bags. Matt still stood there, watching. Jed's father, Dr. Simons and thirteen-year-old Ralph took poles and pushed the heavy boat out into the current.

"Good-by!" yelled Jed. "Good-by, Matt! Take care of Stripy! And catch me a bear!"

Wampum barked joyfully. He too was telling Matt good-by. And he was excited and happy about it.

III

JED SMITH'S GOING WEST!

1. *Pull Away, Boys*

"Looky! There's Binghamton!" Jed shouted. He waved his long arms toward the little cluster of log cabins and mud huts on the banks of the Susquehanna.

"We have certainly made good time today!" Dr. Simons beamed.

"We're going to stop here!" Jed's mother called to Jed and Ralph. They had taken their turn at the oars, which were used mainly to keep the flatboat in midstream.

The boys nodded and went to work with the oars. They tried their best to swing the heavily loaded craft around to head in at the rickety dock. It was too much for them, strong as they

49

were. Mr. Smith and Dr. Simons climbed over the piled-up baggage to help.

They all pulled on the oars. At last the flat nose of the boat swung around. It nudged the dock. Ralph jumped out. He had the end of a heavy rope in his hand. The men worked the boat closer in, and Ralph tied the rope to a post on the dock.

Before it was well fastened, Jed had leaped from the piled baggage onto the dock. Wampum was at his heels. The men stepped ashore and helped the womenfolk. Long dresses made stepping from the boat to the dock a bit difficult.

"Pretty rotten old dock!" Jed said scornfully. He stamped his feet on the planking. "Looks as if it's about ready to fall into the Susquehanna."

Dr. Simons smiled. "But it's going to be repaired and improved," he explained. "Travel's coming this way, Jed. Look!" He pointed to where a broad band of brown earth cut through the grass and trees. It disappeared in the west. "That's the new turnpike."

"Looks like a plain old road to me," Jed answered. "Why is it called a turnpike, anyway?"

Mr. Smith heard the question and answered, "Because the men who own it have built turnstiles at each end. They collect a toll from all travelers. With this money they can afford to keep the road in good repair."

"Well, I don't care which way the travel goes now!" Jed laughed. "We're going to travel right around that road and come out at the other end. The town of Erie is at the other end, isn't it?"

"It's away and beyond the other end of this road," his father assured him.

The family had been walking up the grassy bank toward the houses. Now they saw that folks were coming to meet them.

"Why, Sary Smith!" A woman rushed up to

Jed's mother. "Folks tell that you're moving west. I couldn't believe it."

"Yes, we're moving out," Jed's mother said quietly. "We're heading for Erie, Pennsylvania."

"Do tell!"

"But I had to stop and tell you folks good-by. No telling when we'll see one another again," Mrs. Smith added.

Five or six boys had clustered around Jed.

"Ain't you skeered," one of them asked, "going out where there's nothing but Injuns and wild critters?"

"There are Injuns and wild critters right here in York State," Jed answered. "No, I'm not afraid. I'll kill bears and fight Injuns."

"Oh-oh-oh," chanted another boy, "Jed Smith, the great Injun fighter! Jed Smith, the great bear man!"

The crowd of children took up the yell. They danced about like red men shouting:

"Jed Smith, the Injun fighter!
Jed Smith, the great bear man!"

Jed shook the stubborn strands of brown hair out of his eyes with an angry motion. Then his gray eyes began to twinkle. He added:

"Jed Smith's going west
To see everything he can!"

The boys began to laugh. They crowded closer and started to ask questions.

Jed answered them all. He tried to answer truthfully, but a little bragging crept in now and then. Wasn't he going out to the very farthest edge of things, while these fellows stayed home? He could brag a little, couldn't he?

Jamie Meadows, a big, bullying fellow, lurched against Jed. His shoulder shoved the younger boy. Jed stepped back and stared at him. He didn't understand this kind of action.

"How you goin' to fight Injuns and kill bears?" Jamie asked nastily. "You ain't even got a gun, I bet. Couldn't shoot it if you did have one!"

Jed looked coolly at the other boy. He saw that Jamie carried a rusty old flintlock. Jed's eyes rested on the gun. Golly whackers! A boy not much older than he was, and he had a gun! Suddenly Jed wanted a gun. If only he had one, he'd show them. He could shoot. He'd practiced a few times with Ralph's gun.

"I'll have a gun when I get out west," Jed said quietly.

"Yeah, when you're a man grown! That'll be a far day!" Jamie teased.

"But I wouldn't want a rusty old gun like that," Jed went on. He nodded carelessly toward

Jamie's gun. "Couldn't even hit the side of a barn with that old thing."

"Mebbe *you* couldn't 'cause you can't shoot. But this gun's mighty good!"

Suddenly Jed wanted a gun.

Jed looked around swiftly. He wished he could get hold of Ralph's gun.

Just then he heard old Tim Wilson's voice. The Binghamton trader was asking Jed's father,

"You aim to camp here tonight, or are you going on a piece?"

"We aim to move on," Jed's father answered. "And if we do, we'd better be moving. Come, Sary!" he called to his wife. "Come, children! To the boat!"

Jed looked regretfully at Jamie's gun. Then he shrugged. He'd get a gun! He yelled good-by and turned. Like a flash he was back on the boat calling, "Pull away, boys! Pull away!"

All laughed as they piled onto the heavy craft. They forgot their sadness at leaving old friends.

"You, Jed!" grumbled Ralph good-naturedly. "You pick up the craziest things. Got that 'pull away' from some wandering *voyageur*, I'll wager. Those Canadian boatmen always yell that when they start out."

Mr. Smith put in, "Every time a boat came down-river, Jed was right there, listening to the boatmen's songs and tales!"

"Pull away, boys! Pull away!"

Jed nodded. "Learned a song from 'em, too. Let's sing as we go."

He began to sing:

"From the wilds of the North comes the young
   voyageur,
With his buoyant canoe all laden with fur.
Gladsome and free, little cares he,
For there's joy in the heart of the young
   voyageur."

By the time Jed came to the last line, the whole family had joined in. As they finished, Ralph began to laugh. "Buoyant canoe, my whiskers!" he crowed. "This old flatboat doesn't look much like a buoyant canoe to me!"

Jed giggled. "My whiskers!" he mimicked his brother. "Well, that chin of yours has some fine whiskers, if you ask me!"

Everyone laughed. Ralph put his hand up to

his chin and felt it. He hoped every day to find bristles on his face.

2. *A Job for Everyone*

When the sun's rim touched the hills to the west, Jed's father began scanning the riverbank. "We must find a place to camp for the night," he explained.

"There, Pa!" Jed exclaimed, pointing. "Right over there, see? A little neck of sand, sort of."

Mr. Smith studied the shore. Then he nodded. "Looks right good," he said. "What say, Titus?"

"Excellent!" Dr. Simons agreed. "You have keen eyes, Jed."

Ralph frowned. Jed had always been old Dr. Simons' favorite, just because he liked books. "I saw that place, too," he growled. "I was just waiting to make certain——"

Mr. Smith smiled at the boy. "You're almost a man, Ralph. I count a good deal on your judgment."

Ralph felt better.

They pulled the boat in to shore and tied it fast to a tree. Then they set about making camp.

"Ralph!" their father said. "Take your gun and go into the woods yonder. See if you can't find some fresh meat for supper."

"Let me go too, Pa!" begged Jed.

Mr. Smith shook his head. "Your job is getting wood and water, Jed. In a planned expedition every man has his job. He does it willingly, without a whimper. On our expedition to Erie, your jobs are to gather wood to keep the fires burning, and to fetch water. Now there's plenty of dried wood washed up along this-here sand bar. So skedaddle, son, and bring wood for your ma and the girls to cook with."

Jed turned and went down along the bank. "Pa's right," he thought. There was lots of dry wood here. His job was easy. But he'd rather hunt. Ralph would have all the fun, just because he was older.

"Golly whackers!" he mumbled. "I wish Ma and Pa could see I'm not a baby! I'm past nine, and just about as tall as Ralph, even if he is thirteen!"

He filled his arms with wood and started back to the camp. Suddenly he grinned. "But Pa's right," he said to himself. "Everyone must have a special job. Everyone must obey the cap'n. If ever I'm cap'n, I'll do the same as Pa, I reckon. I'll find out what each man can do best. Then I'll have him do that. And if anyone grumbles, why, I'll—I'll—I'll tan his hide, that's what!" he ended, giggling.

He felt better now. He ran up beside his

mother and dumped the armful of wood. Then
he rushed off for more. Soon he had gathered a
huge pile of fine, dry wood. There was enough
to last all night if they wished to keep the fire
going.

Ralph soon returned. He was carrying a
small wild pig tied to a pole.

Jed saw the proud look on his brother's face.
He heard the exclamations of surprise and de-
light from the others. Again he felt a twinge of
jealousy. Get the meat—that's the one thing he'd
really like to do.

But awhile later, when he sat hunkered on his
heels gnawing a flavorful bone, he forgot his
jealousy. He crept closer to Ralph. "You're a
good hunter, Ralph," he said. "I'm glad Pa sent
you to get the meat."

Ralph smiled at his brother. He, too, felt
good. He was full of roast pig and fragrant corn

bread. "You just wait, Jed. There'll be other chances on this trip for you to learn how to use a gun. I'll ask Pa to let you go with me sometimes."

IV

A CHANCE FOR A GUN

JED and Eunice sat on a stump in front of the little log cabin. It was a fine cabin, Jed thought. And it had been built so fast! No sooner had they arrived at the little settlement on the shore of Lake Erie than neighbors had come. They had helped the Smiths and Dr. Simons put up the cabin.

They had had to hurry to finish it. Something was happening right now inside the big room that was kitchen and sitting room and bedroom all in one. That something was the reason they had had to hurry. It was why Jed and his sister sat watching while everyone else was busy.

They kept within shouting distance at one side of the clearing. Jed could see his father and brother. They were putting up a shed for the cow and the few chickens they had bought.

These animals were the first ones for their new farm.

Sally and Betsey were heating water in a big iron pot over an outdoor fire. When Jed and Eunice offered to help they were told to stay out of the way. There was nothing to do but wait.

Wampum came and put his nose against Jed's hand. He was waiting, too.

Dr. Simons came out the door. There was a wide grin on his round, good-natured face. Jed and Eunice jumped up from the stump and ran to him.

"You have a fine baby brother!" the doctor said. "Now, Jed, you are no longer the baby. You are the big brother."

Jed smiled. "Just as Ralph is to me," he said.

"Can we see him now, please?" Eunice begged.

"Better wait till you're called in," Dr. Simons advised. "Jed, I guess we'll have to skip your lessons today. A new family's come in. I've had word that the mother is pretty sick. If you want to come along, there might be some chores you could do to help out."

Jed glanced toward the cabin. Dr. Simons laughed. "The baby will be there when you get back. And I don't think they'll be calling you for a while yet."

"All right!" Jed fell into step beside the doctor as he started on. Wampum tagged along.

"Well, Jed, how do you like Erie now?" his friend asked. They were making their way toward a branch of French Creek. The new family was camped by the stream.

"I reckon I like it!" Jed answered. " 'Way out here on the edge of things. And Lake Erie! Looks like that ocean you told me about."

"The Pacific." Dr. Simons' voice had a strange sound.

Jed looked up at the man and saw a faraway look in his eyes.

"I had hoped to see it someday myself. That far ocean whose waves lap China's shore!"

Jed's gray eyes looked out across the blue lake. He tried to think what it would be like with China on the other side of it.

"But you'll have to see it for me, Jed. Solomon isn't interested in exploring," the doctor went on. "And when you do, come back and tell me about it. And not only me, but the whole world. That's why I want you to keep on with your studies. Then you'll have the words to describe the things you see."

Jed's eyes were shining with excitement. "I wish I was a man now, so I could set out. If I'd been grown, I might have gone with Captain Lewis and Captain Clark. I'd have been back home now!" His voice shook with the thought.

Dr. Simons chuckled. "The past two years

would have been mighty busy ones, I'll grant you that. And that reminds me. I'm going to have a surprise for you one of these days."

"A surprise? Golly whackers! What kind of a surprise?"

"If I told you that, there'd be no surprise, would there? No, just wait and study and one day that surprise will come. But here we are!"

In a grassy spot beside the stream stood the big wooden wagon in which the new family had traveled. Two small boys were playing on the grass. Their mother sat propped up against a wagon wheel. She was watching them half-heartedly.

Dr. Simons went to the woman. "Hello, there!" he said cheerfully. "I'm Dr. Titus Simons. I heard you weren't feeling too chipper."

"I guess I'm pretty sick," the woman answered. "Sick and hungry. We haven't had much to eat since the old man died. . . ." Her voice drifted away.

Dr. Simons picked up the thin wrist and held it. His firm, gentle fingers were on her pulse. The little boys came close. They stared at the visitors. Wampum went to the boys and sniffed them in a friendly way.

Dr. Simons laid the woman's hand back in her lap. "There's nothing wrong with you that a few good meals won't cure," he said pleasantly. "You're pretty hungry, all right. And those boys look as if they could stand a meal without harm."

He turned to Jed. "Skedaddle up to the cabin and ask your pa for some corn meal and milk. We'll make a fire here and cook 'em up some good corn gruel. That'll do for a start."

Jed nodded. He whistled to Wampum and broke into a run. The dog was right at his heels, eager for a race.

As Jed drew near home, he remembered what

had happened that morning. He stopped running. Eunice had disappeared, so it must be all right to go in. He opened the door carefully.

Mrs. Waggoner, the good neighbor who had come to help, was busy in the kitchen. Eunice was sitting on a little stool beside the big bed. In her arms was a bundle of blankets.

Jed forgot his errand. He tiptoed across the room and looked down at Eunice's bundle. He lifted a bit of the blanket. Jed saw a puckered red face. He stared at it. Then the little face puckered up more than ever. The mouth opened. Jed jumped, scared, as a loud wail came out of that tiny face.

Eunice frowned at her brother. She began to rock back and forth, cuddling the baby. Jed grinned suddenly. This would take care of Eunice for a while. She had had no one but him to play with. She was always trying to tag along with him. Now she could tend the baby, and he could join Ralph in work and fun.

"Isn't he a fine boy, Jedediah?" his mother asked from the big pillow. "We're going to call him Austin. Isn't that a nice name?"

Jed nodded. It was all right. But he liked his own name better. He was glad his parents had named him Jedediah. It was not only his father's name. It was the name also of his great-great-great-grandfather on his mother's side. Jedediah Strong had been killed by Indians at Wood Creek, back in York State. It was really fine to be named for a man who had been a pioneer hero.

Suddenly Jed remembered why he had come. "Ma," he said carefully. He didn't like to bother her, but his father was nowhere to be seen. "Ma, Dr. Simons sent me for some meal and milk. That new woman's hungry. So are her boys, and . . ."

"To be sure!" his mother said quickly. "Caroline!" She raised her voice to attract the attention of Mrs. Waggoner, who was busy at the stove. "Caroline, give Jed a bowl of meal and a bucket of milk. And isn't there an extra loaf of bread? We can't see a neighbor go hungry!"

Mrs. Waggoner bustled about. In a moment Jed was loaded down with milk and meal and bread.

Just this once he thought it would be nice to have Eunice with him. He turned to his sister. "Want to come along?" he invited.

Eunice shook her head. She stopped her low crooning to the baby. "Shh!" she whispered. "I'm getting Austin to sleep!"

Jed felt a little stab of jealousy. It was the first time Eunice had ever refused to go with him. Well! He shrugged his shoulders and set out.

The little boys ran to him as he came near.

"Did you get it?" they demanded. "Did you get it?"

Jed laughed. "I should think you could see!"

"The water is boiling, Jed!" Dr. Simons called. "We'll have gruel ready in half a minute."

Dr. Simons took the meal. He went to a big, black kettle that hung over the fire. Water was boiling in it. He stirred the meal into the water. It bubbled and sent up a little volcano of steam and mush.

The two little boys crowded close. "Where are your bowls?" the doctor asked them. They streaked away to the wagon. They were back again in a moment with three wooden bowls.

Dr. Simons took one of the bowls and spooned it full of the golden-yellow gruel. He held it out to Jed, who poured milk on it. Dr. Simons handed the bowl to the smaller boy.

The little fellow took one hungry glance at

the food. Then he turned and carefully carried the bowl to his mother. Jed was watching. He saw tears come into the woman's eyes as her thin hands took the bowl. "Columbus, you're my good boy!" she said. "Now, go get *your* bowl."

Columbus came running back to the fire. Dr. Simons handed him a bowl of steaming gruel. He dropped down on the ground beside his brother and began to eat hungrily.

Jed wanted to ask about that name, Columbus. But the boys were too busy eating. He didn't like to interrupt them. At last he could stand it no longer. "Is Columbus really your name?" he asked.

The little boy nodded.

"What's yours?" Jed asked the older boy.

"Mine's Marco Polo," the boy answered. "Marco Polo Sackett."

Jed could not believe it. He looked at Dr. Simons. The good doctor gave a friendly smile.

"And mine is Titus Gordon Vespasian Simons!" he said. "There's nothing finer than a good name, is there?"

Jed straightened his shoulders. "Well, mine is Jedediah Strong Smith. That's an explorer's name, too!"

Mrs. Sackett set her bowl on the ground and wiped her mouth on her sleeve. She spoke to Dr. Simons. "Do you know anybody that'd do a mite of hunting for me? We haven't had a smidgen of fresh meat for a long time. I've got a gun." She nodded toward a long shiny "Kentucky" rifle that was propped against the wagon wheel. The brass trimming on the stock gleamed in the sun. "I've kept it close for sort of protection on the road. But if there was somebody—I'd be willing to give him the gun if he'd get meat for us."

Jed bounded forward. "I'll hunt for you!" he said eagerly. "I'll shoot rabbits and squirrels and—maybe a wild pig—maybe a deer." You could shoot almost anything with that long rifle!

The woman smiled wanly. "Sounds mighty good, boy. But you look a mite young to go after meat."

"I'm nine. . . . And I can shoot. Can't I, Dr. Simons?"

Dr. Simons nodded. "Yes, Jed knows how to shoot. Part of the way from his old home in York State he went with his older brother to get meat."

"Well," the woman said slowly, "if your ma and pa say it's all right. You're welcome to the gun, if you'll bring me fresh meat regular. It won't have to be all you bring down, of course. Just enough for me and my boys."

Jed ran to the wagon wheel and picked up the gun. "Golly whackers!" he thought. He'd never hefted anything like that before! He wished Solomon could see it. He ran his finger lovingly over the brass trimming and carefully examined the iron priming pan. "Looks like a mighty good gun," he said admiringly.

"My husband took good care of it, he did. Got it when he went to fight the British. Wasn't much more 'n a boy like you when he fought. Well, you take it along. Maybe if your pa don't want you handling a gun, there'll be the brother the doctor spoke of. He might take the job."

Jed picked up his bucket and bowl. Carrying the long gun carefully, he hurried back to the cabin. Dr. Simons went to his own log house.

Jed wasted no time. He found his father at work and told him what the woman had offered. Mr. Smith examined the rifle and nodded. "Good Kentucky piece, that is! Must be worth quite a chunk of money."

Ralph came and took the gun. His eyes gleamed as he looked it over. He said, "That's

"Looks like a mighty good gun," Jed said.

a danged good piece, Pa. Jed's pretty young. Better let me do the hunting for that woman."

Jed gave a yelp of dismay. "No, Pa! Don't you do it. I got the chance. It's mine. Ralph has a gun of his own. And I can shoot!"

"But that woman needs meat regularly, son. What if you fall down on the job, eh? And you can't go traipsing about the woods alone. I reckon . . . "

"No, Pa, I won't go alone. But I'll do my own shooting. Just let me try. If I can't get meat, I'll—I'll—— Oh, Pa, let me try!"

"Well," his father began slowly, "I reckon it's only fair to let you have a try. But you must promise not to go hunting alone. Ralph or Solomon must go with you."

"All right, Pa," Jed promised. He took the gun from Ralph. His brother seemed to hate to let go of it.

"That's a humdinger of a gun!" Ralph said enviously. "Let's go hunting right now."

"No, Ralph," his father said firmly. "You are busy now, and Jed can certainly find something to do to help Mrs. Waggoner or his ma. Put the gun up, son, and make yourself useful in the cabin."

V

THE TURKEY HUNT

1. *Don't Scare the Birds*

AFTER supper that evening, Ralph and Jed went out to do some chores. Solomon Simons came from his cabin to bring a book the doctor wanted Jed to read. Sol was a big, black-haired boy of fifteen. He laid down his gun and stayed to talk to Mr. Smith for a while. He admired the gun Jed had been given.

"Sol, I hear there's a fine flock of wild turkeys just over the hill," Mr. Smith said. "How would you like to come with me and see what luck we have?"

"Gee, I'd sure like that, Mr. Smith."

Mr. Smith took his gun from the wooden hooks that held it on the wall within easy reach.

He and Solomon began to check their guns carefully.

Just then Ralph and Jed came in. They greeted their friend. "Have you seen my gun, Sol?" Jed cried. "What are you doing, Pa?"

His father smiled. "Neighbor Rutledge says there's a big turkey flock near here. Solomon and I were just getting ready to have a look at them. Want to go, Ralph?"

"Hurrah!" Ralph said.

"Oh, Pa, take me along!" Jed cried. "Please, Pa!"

His father looked at him thoughtfully. "I don't see why not," he said slowly. "Might be a good time for you to learn something about turkey shooting."

Solomon shook his head. "Jed's a bright boy but he's too young, Mr. Smith," he said decidedly. "He'll make a noise and scare the birds. You can't do that if you expect to shoot any turkeys."

"I'll be quiet, Sol. I won't make a sound. Take me along, Pa!"

"I'll watch him," Ralph said.

From her big bed Jed's mother said, "I don't know whether Jed——"

Jed ran and got his gun. "Look what a good gun she is, Pa! Old Grizzly—that's what I've named her. Let me break her in tonight."

His father's gray eyes were measuring Jed carefully. "Jed's growing up, Ma. Time he learned all there is to know about hunting. Jed, get your fixings ready."

"Yippee!" yelled Jed, dancing a little jig. He had never been so excited. "Yippee! Come on, Ralph. Let's get ready."

Ralph snatched up his old gun from the corner where it stood. The two brothers examined their rifles carefully. They brought their powder horns and held them while their father poured in the powder. "I'll give you three balls each—enough for three birds!" he said, smiling. "You'll not be needing more 'n that."

Their mother, propped up on her elbow, watched anxiously. "You'll be careful, Jed?"

"Course I will, Ma."

At last they were all ready. Mr. Smith opened the cabin door and they stepped out into the night.

"Man alive!" Jed's father exclaimed. "Look at that moon! Those turks are going to be easy pickings for us."

Jed was tingling all over. He patted Old Grizzly.

Wampum came bounding toward them. He barked happily. "You'll have to tie that dog up, Ralph," his father said. "We can't have him getting excited and barking. He'd scare the birds."

Ralph led the big dog back to the cabin. He tied him to one of the posts that held up the little porch. Wampum's happy barks became angry yips. Then they turned into mournful howls as Ralph left him and ran to catch up with the others.

2. *They Shoot a Turkey*

The little band moved across the moonlit clearing and into the dark shadows of the trees that covered the hill.

"Where are the turks, Pa?" Jed asked eagerly.

"Just over the hill and down a way," his father answered.

"Now don't start asking questions and jabbering!" Solomon warned. "You got to be quiet when you hunt turkeys. No use to fill the woods with palavering."

Solomon and Mr. Smith strode on. Their long steps took them ahead swiftly. Ralph and Jed had to scramble to keep up. But they didn't care. This was real man's hunting, and excitement made little prickles along the back of their necks.

Under the trees it was very dark. Ralph and Jed kept close together, their arms touching. They kept close behind the older hunters, too. They didn't want to get lost and miss the fun. They all moved quietly, their moccasined feet making no noise. But once in a while a twig would snap, or a low-hanging branch would brush against them. Then they would grow tense and listen.

They all knew that Solomon's warning about filling the woods with noise was not just to keep them from scaring the turkeys. There might be Indians anywhere about here. They'd be a pretty good match for a small Indian band— what with their guns and powder—but they'd rather not meet up with any. It was safest to go quietly.

Up and up they climbed. Jed began to wonder how his father would ever know when they came to the top. Then, while he was still thinking about it, he stumbled and almost fell. They were going downhill! Soon they came out of the trees into a moonlit clearing. Mr. Smith and Solomon stopped. The two Smith boys stopped too, wondering what was the matter.

"Where did Neighbor Rutledge say those turkeys roost?" Solomon whispered to Mr. Smith.

"Half a mile down this side and over to the left. He said there was a bare outcrop of rocks where we turn."

All four peered about them.

"I don't see anything," Jed whispered to Ralph.

"Neither do I," Ralph whispered back.

"You younkers keep still," Solomon reminded them. He was only two years older than Ralph, but two years can make a boy feel much older. "It's down this way, Mr. Smith. I see rocks down yonder."

All four moved forward again, as silently as shadows. Down the slope they went. Each one was watching for the gleam of bare rocks in the moonlight.

Then Jed grasped Ralph's sleeve. "See?" His breath hissed through his teeth in his excitement. He pointed. Off to one side loomed a heap of gray boulders. Jed hurried ahead and touched his father's arm. "Pa!" he whispered. "Look over there!"

His father and Solomon turned. They looked where Jed pointed. Solomon shook his head. "It's this way, Mr. Smith. There are the rocks!"

On the other side of the clearing was another pile of rocks. Mr. Smith looked from one pile to the other. Then he nodded. "I think Sol's right, boys," he said softly. "Looks more like they'd be in that clump of trees over yonder."

Jed shook his head. He didn't know why, but he felt sure the turkeys were near the rocks he had seen. "Let's look around these, Pa," he begged. "Let's just look—then we can go down to those others."

"You and Ralph go look if you want to," Solomon muttered impatiently. "Rutledge said off to the left—that's what your pa told us."

Mr. Smith nodded. "That's right. It must be those farther rocks. Come on, boys!" He and Solomon moved ahead.

Jed hesitated a moment. Then he said, "Let's look over here, Ralph! Crackity! If we're right——"

Ralph looked at his father and Solomon moving down the slope. These rocks were much closer. They could take a peek and then catch up. And if the turks were over there, that would show old Solomon that he wasn't the only fellow who could hunt!

Keeping very close together and walking lightly, the boys hurried toward the rocks. Then they crept around behind the boulders to where the clump of trees stood black in the moonlight. Suddenly Jed stopped. He stared upward. Ralph stopped, too. He looked up.

"Golly whackers!" Jed breathed.

There on the limbs above them, black against the moonlit sky, were scores of wild turkeys. Their big bodies looked strange as they sat there. This one tucked his head under a wing. That one hung his head straight down in front, as if it were just too heavy to take care of.

The boys were glad that their guns were already primed and loaded. Slowly and carefully they raised them and took aim.

Bang! Bang!

Two shots rang out, almost together. The turkeys lifted their heads and looked about. One of the big bodies slowly toppled from its perch and fell to the ground.

"Yippee!" yelled Jed. "I got one! Pa! Sol!" He and Ralph ran forward.

At the first sound of Jed's voice, the turkeys really awoke. The firing hadn't scared them, but the yelling did. As the boys ran toward them, a terrible commotion broke loose overhead. The birds opened their long beaks and let out shrill shrieks. Wings flapped. The turkeys left their perches, flying every which way. It seemed that they had no sense. Screeching and flapping their wings, they filled the night with confusion and noise.

Sol and Mr. Smith came running. Jed kept yelling.

A terrible commotion broke loose overhead.

"Shut up, you fool!" Solomon growled.

Jed flung his hand over his mouth. But it was too late. The turkeys were gone.

"What did I tell you, Mr. Smith!" Solomon said angrily. "Jed's too young to do any real hunting. Why didn't you hush him up, Ralph?"

"Well, I guess I was too excited myself," Ralph said. "But I got a turkey." He pointed to the big, feathered body on the ground.

"*You* got a turkey!" Jed cried. "I hit it—hit it with my Old Grizzly."

By now the screeching and flapping had died away. The turkeys were gone.

"You sure mussed things up, boys," their father said. He was not so angry as Solomon, but he wasn't happy. "You sure spoiled the whole business for us."

"I'm sorry, Pa!" Jed said soberly. "I meant to be quiet. I just went wild when I saw I'd hit a turk——"

"*I* hit it!" Ralph put in, standing over the bird.

"Doesn't make much difference who hit it!" their father said. "Jed did his very best to spoil our chances—mine and Sol's. And you didn't help any, Ralph. There's no use trying to get a turkey now. So pick up your bird, boys, and we'll make for home." He turned away and started up the hill, Solomon beside him.

Ralph and Jed knelt down beside the dead bird. Jed took hold of the big yellow feet. "Golly whackers, it's heavy! I can't lift it."

Ralph took hold. Together they raised the great bird off the ground. "How can we carry it?" Ralph asked. "It's mighty heavy."

"We can bind his legs and slip them over the gun barrel."

"You'd think Pa and Sol would help us," Ralph growled.

"No," Jed said reasonably. "We acted without them. Now they're going to let us get along without them. You can't blame 'em, Ralph."

Jed jerked the buckskin laces out of his shirt and tied the yellow feet together. Then he slipped the long barrel of his rifle under the thong between the turkey's legs. The boys stood up. "You put one end on your shoulder, and I'll take the other," Jed suggested.

Jed lifted the gun butt to his shoulder. Ralph got under the barrel end. They straightened up, and there was the turkey swinging between them. They started up the slope. They wanted to hurry to catch up with the other two. But the big bird slid along the gun and bumped into Jed, who was scrambling behind his brother. They had to stop.

Ahead of them, their father and Solomon had turned and were looking back. Without a word they came and took the gun onto their own shoulders. They could carry the big bird easily.

Ralph and Jed scrambled up the slope. They said nothing. There was nothing to say. They were quiet enough now, as they followed up the hill, through the trees and down the other side.

When they reached the cabin their father hung the turkey high. Jed and Ralph crept onto their blankets under the wagon box. This was their bedroom in the summer.

Solomon went on home. He was disgusted and the boys knew it.

3. *Whose Turkey Is It?*

As soon as it was daylight, Jed slid quietly out from under the wagon. If he showed the turkey to the family before Ralph got up, they might admit that it was his. But Ralph had had the same idea. He crawled out from under the wagon on the other side. They raced for the turkey. They reached it at the same time.

"Look, Ralph," Jed said, "if I don't take that turkey over to Mrs. Sackett, I won't get to keep Old Grizzly."

"And if you do take it," Ralph argued, "we won't have any roast turkey ourselves. I'm hungry for roast turkey—it's been an awful long time since I tasted anything so good as that!"

Jed didn't argue further. Together they lifted the big bird down from its high hook. They carried it into the house.

"Oh, good!" Eunice shouted. "We've got a turkey."

Their father was already at the table with a bowl of hot mush in front of him.

Jed went and stood by his father. "Pa," he said carefully, "I know that Ralph and I both shot— and I don't know how we're going to tell which hit the turkey. But, listen, Pa! I've got to take meat over to Mrs. Sackett——"

Mr. Smith looked at Jed. "It doesn't really matter who killed the turkey," he said quietly. "The law of the hunt is: share and share alike. Since we didn't get any birds, Sol and I, and particularly since that was through your fault, why, the bird should be shared among us all."

Jed knew from the tone of his father's voice that there was no use in arguing. He turned away. Now Mrs. Sackett would think he was not a real hunter. She might even take Old Grizzly back and give it to someone else—maybe to Ralph. He looked at his place at the table. He didn't feel that he wanted any breakfast.

He took Old Grizzly and went out onto the step. He began to clean the gun very carefully. He put an oiled bit of rag on a straight slim hickory stick and rammed it down the barrel.

He wiped out the priming pan. He spat on the rag and tried to polish the brass trimming on the stock. If he had to give Old Grizzly up, he'd leave it slick and shining.

"Jed!" Eunice yelled from the cabin. "Jed!"

Jed got up and went inside, carrying Old Grizzly. He stood by the door, waiting.

"Listen, son," his mother said from her big bed. "I've thought of something. We'll cook the turkey and invite the Sacketts to come and share it with us. I dare say Mrs. Sackett will like that even better than trying to cook it herself, if she is as weak as you've said. That will suit everybody."

They all nodded in agreement. Mrs. Smith went on: "Jed, you go and tell her. And you'd better tell her at the same time just what happened. Then, if she does wish to give the gun to an older hunter, she can do so. At any rate, she'll know that you are a turkey hunter——"

"He won't be a real hunter till he grows up, anyway," Eunice said.

"Oh, yes he will!" Mr. Smith put in. "One mistake doesn't spoil a man for hunting. It just teaches him a lesson—that's all."

"And I've learned my lesson, Pa. I certainly have. I'll never make a sound again when I'm hunting—no matter what! But, crackity, Pa, didn't you ever yell when you hit something?"

Mr. Smith began to laugh, remembering when he was a boy. His face grew red. "Well, now you mention it, I might have *felt* like yelling," he admitted.

Jed shouldered Old Grizzly. "Guess I better get over there, Ma. What time shall I tell her dinner will be ready?"

"It will take a long time to roast that big fellow," Mrs. Waggoner said. "And we ought to have a pie to go with it."

"Tell her to come just before sundown, Jed."

4. *Jed Gets Old Grizzly*

As Jed approached the Sackett wagon, the two little boys came running to meet him. He wasted no time. He told Mrs. Sackett about the hunt. He explained his mistake in yelling and running toward the sleeping turkeys.

"If I'd been real smart, ma'am," he explained steadily, "you'd have had a whole turkey for yourselves. We would have shot more than one. I guess I'm not much of a hunter." He had to gulp over those words. "So Ma thought maybe you'd want to give the gun to someone—someone . . . " He just couldn't finish.

Mrs. Sackett shook her head. "You did right smart, seems to me. You just keep that gun, boy. It's yours now for keeps. I'd far rather have a whole meal than just a turkey—especially since we haven't a thing to go with it."

Jed blinked. He felt a lump in his throat. But

he swallowed it. Golly whackers! Old Grizzly was his, and he'd be plumb certain to act like a real hunter from now on.

"Thankee, ma'am," he said unsteadily. He turned and dashed away. "Won't Ralph be surprised?" he thought.

VI

A MAP FOR JED

1. *Just Bare White Space*

ONE DAY two years later the boys were working in the woods.

Whack! Whack! Whack! Whack!

Jed's ax bit into the chestnut log. He split it through the center. Then he chopped each half into two pieces.

Snack! Snack! Snack! Snack!

The sharp blade of the ax smoothed each quarter log.

Plop!

With one swing Jed buried the ax blade in a tree stump. He swiped his shirt sleeve across his sweaty face. "There they are, Ralph! My fifty are done."

Ralph stopped chopping and rested on his ax handle. "I'll be through in a minute, too. Splitting slabs is tough work. I'll be glad to stop."

Jed split the log through the center.

"Well, we promised John Reed we'd do a hundred today. He wants to get the schoolhouse finished before winter comes. And it takes a mighty lot of these puncheons, standing on end, to make a good solid floor."

Ralph glanced up at the sun. "We'll still have time to go squirrel hunting," he said.

Jed shook his head. "I can't. I've got to go down to Dr. Simons'."

Ralph frowned. "Oh, tarnation! Can't you skip it for once?" he asked impatiently. "What's the good of having a gun if you'd rather have your nose stuck in some old book? Always running over to old Dr. Simons' place!"

Jed chuckled. "You've been going there a bit yourself lately, I've noticed!"

Ralph's face went red. He had hoped that no one had paid any attention to his frequent visits to the Simons' cabin.

"Course, I don't reckon you go there to study, exactly," Jed teased. "Leastwise, I never see you carrying any books. And I know you aren't always visiting Sol."

"Aw, shut up!" Ralph growled and went to swinging his ax again.

Jed saw that his brother was annoyed. "Well," he went on good-naturedly, "I don't blame you any. Louisa's good fun, and pretty, too. Here, give me your ax. I'll take it home for you."

Ralph finished smoothing the last puncheon and handed the ax to his brother. "Tell them to send the wagon out. The puncheons are ready to be picked up."

"Shall I take any word to Louisa?" Jed asked mischievously.

"Wait till you're fifteen!" Ralph muttered. "A younker of eleven like you don't know much!"

Jed smiled. "I may be only eleven, but I'm as tall as you are, Ralph. And I can beat you splitting puncheons, to boot! So I guess I know plenty."

He swung the axes to his shoulder and started away. He whistled as he went.

Wampum had been lazily searching about for something interesting. Now he came loping up. Should he go with Jed or stay with Ralph? Then his yellow eyes lighted on Ralph's gun. He made up his mind. He trotted over to Ralph's side.

Jed dropped the axes in the shed back of the cabin. He went into the kitchen for a glass of milk. He was hungry again. As he drank the milk, two-year-old Austin came running to him. "Jed," the little fellow shouted, "Jed, come play with me!"

Jed looked down at the little boy. "Can't now. Got to go over to Dr. Simons'."

"Take me, too!" Austin begged.

From the cradle came another wail. The new baby, Peter, seemed to be begging to go along.

Jed pretended to frown. "See what you started, Austy!" he scolded gently. "You're big brother to Peter. You must stay and take care of him. Here, play with this."

He reached up and took from a shelf a little wooden gun he had whittled out the night before. Austin grabbed it eagerly. His eyes shone. "I'll go shoot a bear," he yelled. He trotted out of the cabin door.

Jed picked up his books and papers and hurried outside. He chuckled as he passed Austin. The little fellow was "shooting" at a tree stump and shouting, "Bang! Bang!" If he kept on, he'd be able to shoot a real gun by the time he was six.

The thought reminded Jed of how he had learned to shoot when he was nine. He chuckled as he remembered the turkey hunt that had given him Old Grizzly.

"Still the best gun in the family," he muttered. He was about to add, "And I'm the best shot."

But that would be bragging. His parents said bragging was wrong.

A lot of things had happened since they came to Erie. For one, he had learned a great deal. He had read the Bible through from beginning to end. And he had memorized a great many verses. He could read Latin a little. Jed was very proud of that. There was no one else in Erie County, excepting Dr. Simons, he felt sure, who could read Latin.

And he had learned a lot about the West. A long time ago Dr. Simons had given him a wonderful little book. It was the journal of Patrick Gass, a man who had been with Lewis and Clark on their expedition. Gass had been the first member of that party to get out a book. It was a little book, published in Pittsburgh. That wasn't far from Erie, and Dr. Simons had got one of the first copies for Jed. Together the teacher and the boy had studied the journal. They had painstakingly drawn a map to show where the expedition had gone.

"Just think," Jed muttered to himself, "what fun they were having out there while I was still traipsing about the woods in York State!"

The little book was one of Jed's most prized possessions. He remembered how Dr. Simons had surprised him with the gift, and how excited and happy he had been over it.

"I just about know it off by heart now," Jed said to himself. "Golly whackers, I'd like to go out there!"

When he reached Dr. Simons' cabin, Louisa opened the door for him. "You're early, Jed," she said. "Pa isn't home yet. Come sit in the kitchen and have a piece of my squash pie. I'm just taking it out of the oven."

Jed followed the young girl into the kitchen and sat down at the board table. He opened his dog-eared Latin book and began to study.

Louisa plopped a wooden plate in front of him. The smell of the pie, spicy and hot, was too good to resist. He laid his book aside and started to eat.

Louisa was a year older than Jed, but he was so tall and so serious he seemed the older one.

Louisa flounced about the kitchen, tossing her brown curls saucily. "You're the funniest boy, Jed Smith! Not at all like your brother." She stopped suddenly. Her cheeks were rosy. Then she turned to the stove and began fussing with the pots and pans.

The piece of pie disappeared.

"Thanks for the pie, Louisa!" Jed wiped his mouth on his yellow cotton handkerchief. "I reckon you're 'most as good a cook as my ma."

He went into the front room and curled up on the long wooden settee with the bearskin covering. He opened his Latin book and began to read.

Jed was still deep in his book when Dr. Simons came in. He stepped across the puncheon floor with its bear and deerskin rugs and sat down beside the boy. "Still following Caesar?" he asked. "I wish all my students were as eager as you, Jed."

Jed looked up at his friend. Dr. Simons was getting older—not fast, but slowly. His ruddy face, his thick curly white hair, his twinkling blue eyes were as familiar to the boy as the features of his own parents.

Jed shut his book, keeping a finger to mark the place. "It's wonderful!" His eyes were shining. "Just think: why, Gaul—that's France—was almost as wild then as our West is now. Nobody knew a single thing about it. And old Julius Caesar went up there exploring. He came back and wrote it all down. Golly whackers, that was smart!"

Dr. Simons smiled happily. "You and I enjoy

the same things, Jed. We hanker after the same things. I knew you'd like *Caesar*. That's why I taught you Latin."

"Everybody thinks I'm crazy, even Ma. She thinks it's fine that I know the Bible. But Latin!"

Dr. Simons went to a cupboard and opened it. He returned, holding a rolled parchment in his hand. "You speak of our unknown West. Well, Jed, I have just come by a map that shows the entire West. Do you want to see it?"

Jed dropped his book and stood up eagerly. "A map! Of the whole West? Let me see!"

Dr. Simons unrolled the parchment carefully. He smoothed it out on the table. Jed bent over it. The white hair and the brown were close together.

"See!" Dr. Simons' finger pointed to some lines. "Here's where we are. Here's Lake Erie. These are the bay and the island."

Jed's eyes glowed. He was studying the lines

"Here's where we are," Dr. Simons said.

and the dots, and the words in carefully inked letters.

"This line," the doctor went on, "is the Allegheny River. This one, coming up from the southward, is the Monongahela. Here they meet and form the Ohio River. And right where they meet is Pittsburgh."

Jed ran a sun-tanned finger along the line that indicated the Ohio. Suddenly his finger stopped.

"The Mississippi!" he cried. He was as excited as if he had discovered the river itself.

"And the Missouri. Now follow up the Missouri." The doctor's finger moved over the parchment. "This land in here, west of the Mississippi and down to the Arkansas River, then farther south to the Red River—" Dr. Simons' finger pointed—"we purchased from France seven years ago. The land beyond it is Mexico and belongs to Spain."

"Are there lots of Mexicans living there?"

Dr. Simons shook his head. "Not close, I think. Not close to our land. But we don't know. There may be Indians. No white man has ever been into that country and returned to tell what he found."

"Then that's where I'm going!" Jed exclaimed. "I don't want to go where Lewis and Clark went. I used to, but now I want to go *there!*" He put his finger on a wide space on the

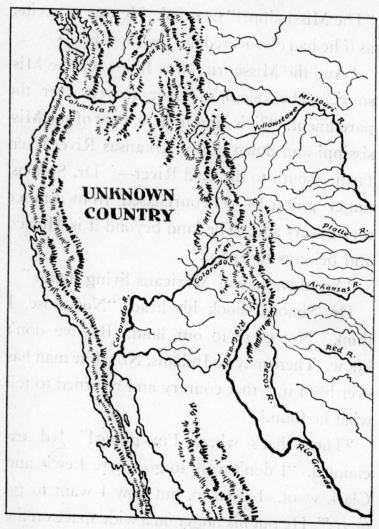

UNKNOWN
COUNTRY

116

map, a space that was empty. There were no wavy lines to show rivers, no little tentlike marks to indicate mountains, no dots for settlements. Just bare white space.

Jed looked up at his teacher. "Why doesn't somebody go there? What are they waiting for?"

"Waiting for someone who has courage and curiosity," Dr. Simons answered. "Maybe you'll be that one, Jed."

"I wish I were a man grown. I'd start out tomorrow."

"The map is yours, Jed. Keep it. Study it. It can't be put to better use."

2. *Fiddle-feet*

When Jed got home that evening he showed his prize to the family. His mother shook her head sadly. "Fiddle-feet," she whispered, "always dancing to a far tune."

"I don't call that much of a tune," Ralph
jeered. "Ain't a thing on that parchment where
Jed's itching to go. Just blank space."

"There's got to be something there," Jed insisted. "There just can't be nothing!"

After the family had gone to bed, Jed sat up.
He whittled a frame to hold his precious map.
The next morning it hung on the kitchen wall.
Jed could look at it while he ate his meals. And
look at it he did, over and over again. Sometimes
he stopped with his spoon halfway to his mouth,
while he stared at the bare place on the map.
He stared and wondered.

VII

JED MEETS A WILD HOG

1. *Too Crowded in Erie*

DINNERTIME at the Smiths' was a big event nowadays. The two new baby boys who had been born since the family came to Erie, added to the older children, made quite a cabinful.

To be sure, Sally was married now and lived over at Waterford with her husband. But when she came visiting and brought her own little boy, why, it made just that many more. There was scarcely room for them all around the big board table.

On this spring day in 1811 they were all there, Sally and her husband, too. And they were all talking.

"I can tell you this," Mr. Smith was saying:

"It's getting too crowded here in Erie. A man can't move his elbow without bumping into someone. Why, just last week we raised a cabin for those new folks—not a quarter mile from here. That's too tarnation close for neighbors!"

Jed's feet moved restlessly on the puncheon floor, made smooth and shining by the constant shuffle of bare feet and moccasins.

Eunice noticed the movement and giggled. "Fiddle-feet!" she teased. "I can see that your feet are itching to dance to a far tune!"

Jed grinned. "Ashtabula, Ohio! Ashtabula, Ohio!" he chanted. "That does make a tune, doesn't it?"

For that's where the Smiths were going now. Erie had become too crowded for Father Jed Smith. And the Indians around Erie were becoming troublesome. Some folks were saying that the British were putting the Indians up to their devilment.

Jed's feet shuffled again on the puncheons. Why should folks ever want to stay in one place? If they got to Ohio, they'd be that much closer to the empty triangle on his map—and closer to Dr. Simons and his family, who had moved on ahead of them.

"Let's go!" he shouted, hardly knowing what he was saying.

His brothers and sisters laughed. They knew how that lanky twelve-year-old loved to explore new places. He had traveled every Indian trail around Erie. Now he was ready for new ones.

2. *Hunter for the Family*

The move to Ashtabula was made that summer. The Smiths piled their household goods into a big wagon and set out through the forest toward the new settlement. It was farther west on the shore of their own familiar Lake Erie.

The Smiths set out toward the new settlement.

By fall the Smiths' cabin was up, and they were settled in their new home, with the Simonses for neighbors.

"Look at that forest!" Jed exclaimed happily one morning. "Bet Old Grizzly will find plenty of work out there!" He patted his gun affectionately. "Think you can find time to go hunting with me?" he teased Ralph.

Ralph's face got red. Ever since they had reached Ashtabula Ralph had spent more time over at the Simons' cabin than he had with his brother.

"It's a good thing Dr. Simons came out here before we did!" Jed went on. "If he hadn't, I'll wager Pa couldn't have dragged you out here with a logging chain."

"Don't worry about Ralph," their father put in, chuckling. "You ought to be happy that he has other interests, because—" he paused a moment and Jed waited expectantly—"you're going to be official hunter for the family. You're going to be the meat getter now."

Jed's eyes glowed with excitement. "Honest? Golly whackers! Old Grizzly will be busy then."

3. *Wampum Is a Hero*

On an evening in December Jed was returning home with the meat of a deer he had killed. He had had bad luck that day, and had been forced to use up his last charge of powder to get a young buck. Then he had skinned it and cut off as much of the good meat as he could carry.

At his side trotted old Wampum. The dog was not much use as a hunter now, because he was getting old and stiff. Still, whenever one of the boys went out carrying a gun he had to trot along.

As Jed made his way among the trees he kept a wary eye on his surroundings. It wouldn't do to meet up with a wild animal now that his gun was useless.

"There's a time for everything," Jed said to the old dog, "and right now isn't the time for meeting some hungry wild critter. Old Grizzly wouldn't be any help." He frowned, thinking of that last muzzleload of powder he had poured down Old Grizzly's throat.

"Pa would say I was a mighty poor specimen of a hunter, using up my last powder that way," he muttered, "when I still have to go through woods. But what's a fellow to do when a deer stands there, daring him to shoot? And meat needed at home——"

He shifted the weight on his shoulder. His moccasined feet moved swiftly and surely along the homeward trail. It was growing late and there was no time to waste. Even Wampum seemed eager to get home. He dashed ahead of Jed along the trail.

"Not that we're scared!" Jed went on, with a feeble grin. "We're just cautious. Anyway, Pa says caution makes the difference between a hunter and a fool."

The words were hardly out of his mouth when he heard a strange sort of grunt behind him. Old Wampum whirled. The fur on his neck stood on end. He gave a low growl. Jed turned.

There, coming toward him in a mad rush through the trees was a vicious stray hog. His head was down. His murderous teeth were bared. His ugly little eyes were red with anger.

Jed dropped the meat from his shoulder. He dropped Old Grizzly. He took to his heels. He yelled for Wampum to follow. If he could just make it to that tree——

But Wampum, for once, did not obey. He looked at the hog and his old fighting spirit stirred. He forgot he was old and stiff. Back went his lips in an angry growl. He braced his legs. He hunched his shoulders.

Jed, seeing that Wampum wasn't with him, hesitated, turned. He saw the old dog give a leap at the hog.

The enraged animal swerved just enough to rush straight at the dog. The great yellow teeth dipped down and thrust forward, but Wampum danced out of their reach.

Jed shuddered and groaned as an upswing of the teeth caught Wampum in the side. Blood spurted from the gash. But Wampum kept on fighting. As the hog ducked his head to attack again, Wampum grabbed him by the ear.

The beast gave a loud roar of pain.

Jed could stand still no longer. Anger made him forget caution. He forgot that he was just a boy, that he had no protection, that he had no powder for Old Grizzly. He ran back toward the fighting animals. He stopped only to pick up his gun as he ran. He had no idea what he was going to do except he knew he must save Wampum from that murderous attack.

The hog seemed to understand that a new menace was threatening him. He turned from Wampum to Jed. He darted at the boy, but Wampum still clung to his ear. It hindered the hog's rush, while the pain maddened him.

The animal shook his head viciously, trying to shake off Wampum's hold. But he came on toward Jed.

Jed dodged. Moving fast, he got around behind the beast. He raised Old Grizzly and struck the hog as hard as he could on the hips. This brought the animal's hindquarters to the ground. Using Old Grizzly as a club, Jed hit the hog again and again.

The beast grunted in pain and squealed with anger. But with Jed's blows on his hips and Wampum fastened to his ear he was almost helpless. Suddenly Jed saw that Wampum's strength was failing. He'd have to do something quick. If the dog lost his hold, the hog would be free to turn on Jed.

He must do something!

While he was beating at the hog he tried frantically to think of a way of escape. Then he remembered what his father did when he had to disable a steer he was going to butcher.

Jed snatched his sharp hunting knife from his belt. He moved in close to the beast. As the animal struggled to rise, the boy stooped and cut the big tendon above the hock. The hog sat down, helpless.

"Wampum," Jed yelled, "let go! Here! Here, boy! He can't hurt me now!"

The old dog was too far gone to respond. As the helpless, hamstrung hog threshed his head about, Wampum was flung aside. Jed stepped in and with one stab finished off the crazed beast.

He ran to Wampum, who lay covered with blood and panting on the snow. The boy looked at his friend. Then he jerked off his heavy home-spun shirt. He knelt on the ground and gently lifted the dog onto the garment. Then he picked him up carefully and started homeward at a trot.

Mr. Smith saw Jed coming across the clearing, all bloody and dirty and carrying a blood-soaked bundle. He came running. "What is it? Are you hurt? Where's your gun?" he asked rapidly.

Ralph came around the cabin. Jed's mother and the girls hurried out. The little boys followed.

Jed laid his bundle gently on the ground and opened it up. Old Wampum lay stiff and still. Only his heaving flanks showed that he was still alive.

Austin and Peter began to cry.

"Fetch warm water, Eunice!" Jed's mother

ordered crisply. Eunice dashed to the house. She returned with the wooden basin filled with warm water. She had thought to bring a cloth, too.

Jed knelt and held Wampum's head while his mother gently bathed the wounds.

"What happened, son?" his father asked.

"He's a real hero, Pa. He tried to save my life. And he did save it. I hope——" The words caught in his throat.

Wampum heard his voice. He opened his eyes. He put out his long tongue and licked Jed's hand. Tears came into Jed's eyes.

Then, while Mrs. Smith gently smoothed the wet fur, Ralph got sugar and soap. He kneaded them together to make a salve. They rubbed this into the gaping wounds.

When, at last, old Wampum was peacefully sleeping on a soft blanket on the little porch, Jed told the story of the battle. As he talked, his father shook his head in wonder. His mother shuddered and flung her arms about him.

"I never heard tell of such a thing!" Mr. Smith said. "A twelve-year-old younker killing a wild hog!"

"Not just me, Pa!" Jed insisted. "Me and Wampum."

"Let's go see!" Ralph urged.

"Yes, we must go. And we must get Jed's meat, too, and his gun. Come along, boys."

Ralph started with his father. Jed dashed ahead. "I'll show you the way," he cried. "Come on!"

VIII

JED TAKES A MAN'S JOB

JED was in Detroit. He walked steadily through the streets of that bustling port town. But he kept his eyes open. He had his sea bag on one shoulder. His gun, grasped loosely in his hand, hung by his side after the fashion of good woodsmen.

He didn't have to ask the way to the dock. From the center of town he could see the masts of the ships. Jed went toward them. When he reached the dock he stopped. He studied the names printed in bright paint on the prows. His heart began to thump as he came to the one he was looking for—the *Cheboygan*.

Jed had come a long way for this. On foot, with only Old Grizzly to provide him with food, he had tramped all the way from Ashtabula to

Cleveland. There he had found a job as cabin boy on a ship sailing to Detroit. He had served so well that now he had in his pocket a note from the captain to the master of the *Cheboygan*. And he had also a letter from Dr. Simons to this same captain.

The *Cheboygan!* Jed thought of the far northern woods where buckskin-clad men had been busy all winter trapping beaver, otter, mink and other wild animals. The *Cheboygan* would carry salt, lead, traps, sugar and tobacco up to those dark woods. There the men would load the ship with furs and bring them back to make hats and cloaks and robes for the people of the cities.

It was very early in the morning and the dock was quiet. Jed was pleased. It would be the best time to see Captain Marks and ask for a job as cabin boy. His long legs carried him up the sloping gangplank and onto the deck.

A heavily bearded sailor leaned against the rail. "Avast there, matey!"

Jed grinned. It sounded as if he were already a sailor. "Can you tell me where I'll find Captain Marks?"

"In his cabin, where any self-respectin' cap'n should be this time o' morning." The sailor nodded carelessly toward the stern of the ship.

Jed's recent experience on the *Sea Horse* helped him now. He made his way to the captain's cabin under the raised afterdeck. Jed dropped his sea bag and knocked. At a curt "Come in!" he opened the door and entered.

His eyes went to the man sitting in a heavy wooden chair behind a long table. He did not take time to notice the thick carpet on the floor, or the polished brass of lamps, knobs and railings.

Captain Marks, Jed saw, was a short, heavyset man. He had bushy, iron-gray brows that almost met across the bridge of his nose. Under those brows were piercing blue eyes. But at the corners of the eyes were the telltale laugh crinkles that reveal a sense of humor.

"Captain Marks, sir?" Jed asked.

"Yes, lad! Step up and speak out your business with me."

"I carry two letters to you, sir. One from Dr. Titus Simons of Ashtabula, Ohio. He knew you as a boy in Vermont———"

Captain Marks stood up and extended his hand, smiling. "*Doctor* Simons!" he exclaimed. "Well, well, it's been years since I heard from him. He was plain *Mister* Simons then. Give me the letter, lad."

Jed took the letter from his pouch and handed it to the man. As he read, Captain Marks glanced up from time to time at the boy. When he had finished he said, "You said two letters?"

"Yes, sir. The other is from Captain Goddard

of the *Sea Horse*. I worked my way up from Cleveland on his ship."

He held out the second note. It was on soiled paper and poorly written. Captain Goddard was not so neat as Jed's old teacher.

Captain Marks read the second note. He

Captain Marks read the second note.

smiled again. "So you're only thirteen!" he remarked. "A tall lad, and well built. You should be of good use aboard the *Cheboygan*."

"Then you'll employ me, sir?" Jed asked eagerly.

The captain nodded. "Cabin boys are as cheap as old towrope, and about as trustworthy. When I can find one that comes recommended, I anchor onto him. But it isn't just because your friends give you a good character. It is this." He laid his finger on a line in Dr. Simons' letter.

Jed knew what that line said: "The boy can write a neat hand, cipher rapidly and accurately, and understand French fairly well."

"Those are accomplishments I've never found before in a cabin boy. And they'll be worth money to you on this trip, lad. I'm going to ship you on as junior clerk. Though—" the captain held up his hand as he saw the excitement in Jed's eyes—"you'll have to act as cabin boy, too.

Père Jean, the cook, needs help and you'll assist him. Your duties as clerk won't take much time. And to make the voyage profitable, each man must do everything he can."

Jed nodded eagerly. "Yes, sir!"

"On the voyage up and back, you'll help Père Jean in the galley."

Jed smiled to himself. Helping in the kitchen, he would have plenty to eat, that was sure.

Captain Marks went on: "But when we get to the fur fields, you'll keep tally of the peltries— the furs—that are brought in. You'll put down the payment made to each trapper. Your pay will be five dollars a month. You'll get your money at the end of the voyage, when we return to Detroit."

Then the captain's shrewd blue eyes fell on Old Grizzly. Jed's hand still held the gun. "You won't be needing that, lad. I'll take charge of it."

Jed glanced down at the gun. Then he looked

up at the captain and a wide smile spread across his face. "I'd forgotten Old Grizzly, sir. But he sure came in mighty handy when I was traipsing through the woods."

"You're a hunter, too? Well, maybe you'll get a chance at game up in those north woods."

Jed handed Old Grizzly to the captain and turned to leave.

"One moment, lad," Captain Marks said. "It hasn't escaped me that you know how to say 'sir.' And that is good. It will save teaching you the first requirement of ship duty—courtesy. And obedience. And now, before you sign the ship's register, tell me: how does it happen that a woodsman seeks employment on shipboard?"

"I need money, sir. And there's no money in the woods. Our family is large. There are three brothers younger than I at home." Jed felt a sudden homesickness to see the little boys. Three now: Austin, Peter and Ira. How could his father ever educate them all?

Captain Marks came around the table and laid his hand on Jed's shoulder. "So you take your place as a man, eh? Well, that's fine. Now report to Père Jean in the galley. He'll show you what you're to do and where you're to sleep. The men will be coming aboard soon from their last shore leave. Then we'll weigh anchor and set sail."

Outside the cabin door Jed picked up his sea bag. He went along the deck toward the galley, a small room built up on the deck between the main hatch and the foremast.

Squatted on the deck beside the galley door was an old Frenchman. He had long gray locks almost covered by a round knit cap. His leather-brown face was wrinkled. His eyes were closed as he soaked up the sunshine of the early spring morning.

"Père Jean?" Jed began softly.

The wrinkled lids lifted and two sleepy brown eyes looked up.

"I'm your new cabin boy. My name is Smith."

The old man shrugged and closed his eyes again.

Jed looked around. He thought, "It's certainly the quietest ship that ever was! Nothing like the *Sea Horse*. That was all noise and brawling."

Just at that moment he heard a familiar sound. Sailors were coming along the dock. They were singing and laughing. This was more like it.

Up the gangplank they came, and along the deck. They pushed and shoved one another. As they came even with the galley, Jed jumped back out of their way. But he was not quick enough.

One big fellow caught the boy's sleeve and swung him around. "Well, blow me down," he cried, "if it ain't a new cabin boy! Course I knew Cap'n would have to get one after what happened to t'other lad."

The others roared with laughter and crowded close to Jed.

"Did ye hear about that, lad? We strung t'other boy up to the yardarm. He swung there like a rag." The fellow motioned above him and the others looked up. It seemed as if they could see the other boy swinging up there—hanging from the wooden beam that stretched its two arms across the tall spar.

Jed smiled at them. He was thankful that he'd found out about this kind of joking on the *Sea Horse*. It had been tough at first but now he knew that it was just a part of becoming a sailor.

One of the men reached out a hairy paw to grab Jed's shoulder. But before the huge fingers could close, Jed was given a sharp push by Père

Jean. He tumbled backward, through the galley door and onto the floor of the little room.

Père Jean stepped in after him, agile as a monkey. He closed and bolted the door. "Baboons!" he muttered.

Outside the galley now all was noise and excitement as the men made ready to cast off. Jed listened. He wanted to be outside. He wanted to share the thrill of seeing the ship leave the wharf.

The old Frenchman was watching him. He seemed to know what the boy was thinking. After a moment or two he nodded. Jed quietly opened the door and stepped out.

The sailors were too busy now to notice him. Jed felt the rocking motion of the ship and saw the water between ship and dock grow wider. The *Cheboygan* was moving.

IX

DANGER ON LAKE HURON

1. *Trouble with the British*

"Joyful, joyful, without a care,
My canoe, my canoe!"

THE woods were filled with song and chatter.
Down the rivers and streams that fed Lake
Huron from the north came the long canoes.
They were piled high with furs. They were
manned by trappers in red wool shirts, knit
caps, and brown or blue woolen trousers. Along
the narrow paths between the trees came other
trappers, with their peltries on their backs. They
were coming to trade their furs on the *Cheboygan* in exchange for supplies.

Jed stood beside an upended barrel. His little
stone crock of heavy black ink was on the barrelhead. His quill pen was poised, ready to write
down the furs that were traded.

Beside Jed stood Jock McDonal, second mate of the *Cheboygan*. He was receiving the furs. Around these two crowded the trappers. There were copper-hued Indians dressed in the skins and furs of the northern Chippewa. There were French-Canadians, ragged and long-haired. There were a few Yankees who had decided that the free life of the trapper was more to their liking than the quiet life of a villager.

Each trapper would step up before Jock and fling down his pack of "plews," as they called their pelts. Then the trapper would stand there, watching the buyer with crafty eyes. Jock would count the pelts and sing out the result to Jed.

"Twenty prime beaver!"

"Forty elk hides!"

"Seventeen otter!"

Jed's quill scratched on the rough paper.

Jock paid the men from sacks standing open beside him. If it was an Indian, he would give

Jed's quill scratched on the rough paper.

him a handful of blue beads, a small, brass-bound looking glass, or some tobacco.

If it was a Canadian trapper, Jock paid him in woolen goods, salt or powder. And if it was a Yankee, he would offer new traps or tobacco.

Money was used in trading only as a last resort.

After a while there was a lull in the trading.

"Jock," Jed said softly, "you do not pay them all the same. Those Indians, now——"

Jock frowned. "You mind your business, lad, and I'll attend to mine!"

Captain Marks overheard Jed's remark. He spoke to the boy. "And what good would silver be to them, eh, lad? We pay them in the coin they desire."

Jed's gray eyes looked up frankly at the man. "But, sir, those beads are worth only a few coppers. And the peltries they've brought will bring many dollars in Detroit."

"That's true, lad. That's how we make our profit. And little enough profit it is, to be sure! The peltries these trappers bring in to us are their poorest. They're peltries the British wouldn't purchase at any price!" His tone was bitter.

"Why, sir, don't they bring us their best furs? Why do they give the British first choice?"

"Because our trading rivals have for years been telling them that we are scoundrels. And so, in a manner of speaking, they force us to behave like scoundrels." He kicked open a bundle of furs.

"Look at those pelts!" he said. "They were stored while they were wet. They're practically valueless. They're not worth much more than a handful of beads."

A thought flashed into Jed's mind. "Why don't we go where there are no British?"

"And where would that be, lad?" Captain Marks asked gently.

"At home I have a map," Jed said eagerly. "There's a wide place on it where no one has ever been. At least, no one has ever told about being there. Dr. Simons says——"

"Then I'll wager there are no beaver there,"

Captain Marks said and laughed. "Wherever there are beaver, the British have set up posts to rake them in." The captain's frown grew darker. He stared into the woods that surrounded them.

"And that's not all, lad!" he muttered gloomily. "The British are growing more daring every day. Trouble's brewing wherever they are. It's a shame the government doesn't give General Hull more troops. He could wipe them out of these forests."

"Plews! Plews!" yelled a bearded Frenchman. He dumped a scraggly pack at Jock's feet. Jed went back to his tallying. But he was beginning to have an idea.

2. *War!*

July came. The last trapper had brought down his furs, received his pay, and disappeared again into the dark forest. The long canoes had vanished up the rivers. The *Cheboygan* was loaded and ready to start on the long journey back across Lake Huron.

"We'll lift anchor at dawn," Captain Marks instructed the crew.

Jed spoke up quickly. "Why don't I take Old Grizzly and get one more deer for us to enjoy on the way back?"

"That's a fine idea," the captain agreed. "I don't know how we'd have managed without you and Old Grizzly. You've brought us many a fine meal."

Jed got his gun and went to the rail. He was ready to swing over the side and climb down into the skiff. Two men were waiting to row him ashore.

A sudden call from the shore made Jed stop and look up. On the bank stood a ragged figure. He was yelling and motioning. He tottered as if he could scarcely stand. He waved wildly.

"Stay, lad!" Captain Marks ordered. Jed drew back from the rail.

"Hallo, the shore!" yelled the captain. "What is it you want?"

"News! News from Mackinac!" shouted the ragged man.

"Go bring him aboard," the captain ordered the men in the skiff.

They dipped their oars and made for the shore. The other members of the crew crowded to the rail, watching. Even old Père Jean came out of his galley and watched with the others.

In a short time the skiff was back. The stranger clambered up onto the deck. The oarsmen followed at his heels.

"Now what have you to tell us?" Captain Marks demanded.

"War! War! It's come! It's here!"

"War?" the sailors echoed.

"Yes. We've declared war on Great Britain. But she's taken the first trick. This lake is in her hands. She has seized Mackinac. Your life ain't worth a farthing if you try to go back across Huron."

"But, man——" the captain began, and stopped. Then he said, "How did you get here?"

"When the commander at Mackinac saw the island was bound to fall into British hands, he sent runners out to warn the American ships along the shore. He hoped to save some."

"And our thanks to him!" the captain cried. He added with determination, "But we'll have to make a run for Detroit."

"And much good that'll do you, if I may speak my mind. The British are lying in the lake before Detroit. The Indians surround the city on the land side. An eel couldn't slip through that blockade."

"We'll have to. We can't lie here all winter. And it would be no safer."

Captain Marks looked at his crew. The men stood silent. Their faces were scowling and glum.

Suddenly the captain's shoulders straightened. He spoke heartily. "We'll make it, lads! With a staunch crew and clever sailing, we'll dodge the British and make it through to Detroit, I promise you!"

The men looked about at one another. Their faces were still dark and gloomy. Then they looked out over the blue waters of the lake. There was home. There must be safety.

"And we'll not be waiting till dawn to weigh anchor," Captain Marks went on as if the whole crew stood heartily behind him. "To your places, men!"

"But set me ashore first," begged the messenger. "Give me something to eat and drink, and then I'll be off to warn others of the danger."

Père Jean and Jed ran to the galley. The boy carried a plate of food to the fellow. Père Jean packed meat and bread for him in a cloth.

When the messenger had eaten, the skiff took him ashore. By the time it returned, the *Cheboygan* was ready for sailing. The two oarsmen climbed aboard. The skiff was lashed to the ship. In silence the anchor was raised and the little ship set out into the dangerous twilight.

3. *Capture or Escape*

"Sail, ho! Sail to windward!"

The call caught everyone aboard the *Cheboygan* by surprise. Perhaps they had grown a bit careless. They had sailed now for several days but they had sighted nothing to alarm them. Lake Huron, in fact, seemed to be utterly deserted except for the little *Cheboygan* and the wild sea birds.

"What do you make her to be?" Captain Marks shouted to the sailor high up in the crow's-nest.

"It's a brig, sir. It's steering toward us at good speed."

Captain Marks put his glasses to his eyes. But he could see nothing from the deck.

The wind was strong, and the *Cheboygan* was making good time under her sails. Perhaps there was no cause for alarm. The captain, however, still scanned the horizon to the northeast.

"I can see her now!" he exclaimed. "But only the topgallant sail. I can't yet make her out."

"She's British, sir!" called the lookout now. "And she's gaining on us."

"We can't fight!" the captain muttered. "But we won't be captured if we can help it. Tom Maycock," he called to the sailing master, "hoist

"Sail, ho! Sail to windward!"

every inch of canvas! Take advantage of this wind. We're going to run for it."

Tom nodded, agreeing. Then he said, "We're lighter than she is, sir. Maybe we can outrun her." He hurried away.

Now the deck was filled with confusion as the captain shouted orders. "Sand the deck! 'Twill give us better footing if we have to fight hand to hand. Get your muskets ready." The men flew about.

Jed grasped Old Grizzly. He felt excitement burning through his whole body. This was war. He'd heard about the British ships with their twelve-pounders that could blast a hole in the side of any ship within range. The little *Cheboygan* was not equipped for warfare. She wouldn't have a rabbit's chance if the Britisher caught up with them.

Down the wind they raced. The men stood tense along the rail. Even without glasses they could see that the brig was gaining on them. Closer and closer she came. Larger and larger loomed her hulk. The British flag, the Union Jack, was flying at her mizzenmast. It seemed to laugh at them. The orange-painted mouths of her guns glared at them through the portholes. They waited, breathless, for those guns to spout fire.

And then, with a suddenness that nearly upset the watching men, the ships stood still. Without warning the wind had stopped. The lake became deadly calm. The sails hung slack.

The men looked at one another. They turned to their captain. Then they looked back at the British ship. They shook their heads.

"We're out of gun range," Captain Marks said thankfully. "But just barely so. And what good that will do us the minute the wind picks up again, I'm sure I don't know." He chewed

at the edge of his beard. A dark frown was between his brows.

"Well, she can't move now," someone said
hopefully.

Captain Marks made up his mind. "Look,
you!" he cried to the men. "Bring every spare
hawser on the ship!"

The men stared at him for a moment and then
disappeared. They came back carrying the
heavy ropes used to tie the ship to the dock.

"Splice them together!" Marks barked. "Make
haste!"

The men joined the ropes securely.

"Now take the kedge anchor. Fasten this
hawser to it! Man the skiff!"

Now the men understood what their captain
wanted. They worked with feverish speed. They
put the small anchor into the skiff. They lowered
the little boat over the side of the *Cheboygan*.
They did their best to keep their movements hid-

den from the enemy. Once in the water, they rowed out as far as the spliced hawser would permit. Then they dropped the anchor.

On deck, the crew grasped the rope. They pulled with all their might. The *Cheboygan* began to slip through the water. Hand over hand, the crew "walked up" the rope, pulling as they moved along. The *Cheboygan* crept ahead.

Jed, pulling with the rest, couldn't help glancing back. He saw Captain Marks raise his glasses and look toward the Britisher. Then he came to the sweating, pulling men.

"They don't know what to make of it, I'll wager!" He chuckled gleefully. "Keep at it, men! Keep at it! We're moving slowly, but three knots is a better speed than nothing!"

As the *Cheboygan* neared the end of the rope, the men in the boat lifted the anchor and rowed away. When they had gone as far as the length of the rope would permit they dropped the anchor again. And again the crew pulled the *Cheboygan* ahead.

Three hours of this, and Jed's hands were raw and bleeding. He felt that he must drop in his tracks. He had never been so tired in all his life.

Then, as if to help the gallant little ship, the wind sprang up again. The sky grew black, and the rain fell in a heavy downpour. The darkness and the rain hid the *Cheboygan* from the Britisher. Sails were hoisted in a split second. Like a terrified sea bird, the little craft sped through the lashing storm.

Late that afternoon the sun broke through the clouds. The rain and wind stopped. The men on the *Cheboygan* looked back. There was no sight of their pursuer. They had outrun the enemy. They were safe now.

Their escape filled them with confidence. But they did not grow careless again.

4. *Golden Coins*

A few nights later the *Cheboygan*, under cover of darkness and rain, slipped past the blockade at Detroit and safely reached port. Captain Marks lost no time. He paid his men and dismissed them.

"General Hull will surrender Detroit to the British before many days," he told the crew. "Better get away before that unhappy day comes."

Jed was one of the last to leave the ship.

Captain Marks handed him four golden coins. There was one for each month of his service on the *Cheboygan*. "Where will you be going, lad?" the captain asked him kindly.

"I reckon I'll go home," Jed answered. He clinked the golden coins in his pocket. "I came out to get money to help the family. Now I have it, I'll set my feet on the back trail."

X

OFF TO ADVENTURE

ONE afternoon in late winter, nearly ten years after he had said good-by to the *Cheboygan,* Jed strode along the snowy trail that traced the southern shore of Lake Erie. On his back was the pack of peltries he had trapped that winter, over on the Rock River in northern Illinois. In his buckskin pouch was his Bible and a torn and yellowed scrap of newspaper.

Jed had walked a long way since he had been given that scrap of paper. But he was nearly home now. Every little while he met some old neighbor. He would stop to pass the time of day and make inquiries about the news of the place. But Jed did not tarry long. He was in a hurry.

When at last he saw the Smith cabin, with smoke curling from the big stone chimney, he could scarcely keep his long legs from breaking into a run. Home! It was good to be home.

He pushed open the door.

"Jed! Jedediah!"

"It's Jed come home!"

His mother flew to him and threw her arms about him. His father pumped his hand up and down. The boys crowded around. There were no girls left in the Smith cabin. Betsey had married an Ohio boy. Eunice was married to Solomon Simons, Jed's old friend. Ralph was married to Louisa Simons. They had cabins of their own. But the younger members of the family were home—Austin, Peter, Ira, Benjamin and the "baby" of the family, Nelson, a boy of seven.

"What good fortune brings you home, son?" his father asked when food had been set before the traveler.

Jed fished into his pouch and brought out the slip of paper. "Read that, Pa."

Nelson scampered to get his father's glasses with their square lenses and steel bows. Then Mr. Smith read to the family:

TO

Enterprising Young Men

The subscriber wishes to engage ONE HUN-DRED MEN, to ascend the river Missouri to its source, there to be employed for one, two or three years.—For particulars enquire of Major Andrew Henry, near the Lead Mines, in the County of Washington, (who will ascend with, and command the party) or to the subscriber, at St. Louis.

(Signed) WILLIAM H. ASHLEY
Feb. 13, 1822

"I'm going to St. Louis," Jed said when his father finished. "I'm going to answer that advertisement. Major Henry has already been up the Missouri and trapped there. The fellow who gave me this notice said that General Ashley plans to trap beaver away out and beyond the Shining Mountains. I've wanted to go there for years. This is my chance."

His father nodded slowly. "I don't blame you, son. I've always looked toward the West myself."

"And lived as far west as you could get with a family!" Jed chuckled. "Well, I'm alone. I can go anywhere."

Jed stayed only that one night at home. In the evening his old friend and teacher, Dr. Simons, came to the cabin. The two sat up late, looking at Jed's old map. They talked of the unknown places in the West.

The next morning Jed set out. He carried only a small pack. In it were the new hose his mother had knit while he was away. There were a new striped hickory shirt and two yellow cotton handkerchiefs. There were a little flagon of ink, a quill pen and an empty book in which to write

The next morning Jed set out.

down his travels. And there were a hymnbook
and a Bible.

Over his shoulder was slung Old Grizzly. At
his waist hung his powder horn and pouch. He
was ready for anything.

"Good-by, Ma!" he said, stooping to kiss her.
"Good-by, Pa!" They shook hands.

"Good-by, boys!" he called to his brothers.

"Good-by! Good-by!"

They stood in the cabin dooryard, in spite of
the raw March day. They watched the tall, strid-
ing figure until it disappeared among the trees.

XI

JED'S DREAM COMES TRUE

ONE sultry August day in the year 1826 four tall and tanned Mountain Men sat in their camp on the shore of the Great Salt Lake. They were discussing the new company they had just formed. Three of them—Captain Jed Smith, Davy Jackson and Bill Sublette—had recently purchased General Ashley's Rocky Mountain Fur Company. The fourth, Tom Fitzpatrick, was their friend, companion and employee.

Now the trappers had gathered together to discuss plans and problems in managing their newly formed company.

"Let's call our company Smith, Jackson and Sublette," Davy Jackson suggested. The others agreed.

"And let's carry on the way General Ashley did," Bill Sublette offered. "Let's not build expensive trading posts as the British do. We'll have a big fur fair, or rendezvous, each summer as we did last summer. The free trappers and the Indians like that. It's something to look forward to—all coming together in one place to sell their furs and buy new supplies."

"And let's seek out new territory for trapping," Jed put in.

The others chuckled. "Well, when we divide our duties, I know who will be chosen for that branch of the work," Bill Sublette said.

Davy nodded in agreement.

"Yes, Jed, you take over the exploring end," Bill suggested. "Davy, here, has been wonderful at managing the trappers and Indians. So he can handle the collecting of the furs. And I guess that leaves me to take the peltries to St. Louis."

Jed brushed back the long brown hair that fell over his forehead. The movement revealed a terrible scar that reached across his face. His eyebrow was twisted by the scar in a way that gave him a quizzical expression.

The scar reminded his three companions of the worst moment in their lives. That had been three years ago when Jed had been attacked by a huge grizzly bear. Too close to shoot, Jed had fought desperately with his knife. But he had been no match for the raging beast. The bear had clawed one side of Jed's face, tearing his right ear badly, and had broken several ribs before a shot from a companion's gun had saved the young captain.

But Jed was not thinking of that fight. His gray eyes were staring southward. "I'll start as soon as possible," he said with decision. "I'll take only about fifteen men. A small party can travel more swiftly and safely than a large one."

Jed picked his little band with care: good hunters, a blacksmith, a couple of men trained in the care of horses, and an interpreter who knew a little Spanish. If they reached the Mexican villages, they would need someone to speak for them. Jed packed his supplies with equal care: guns and powder for his own men; tobacco, blankets, tools and trinkets to trade for furs and provisions.

"We can't carry much food," Jed observed. "We'll trust to our guns and our knives."

Southward traveled the little band, following the valleys. Each valley seemed rimmed with mountains. But always Jed rode ahead. His gray eyes were always on the farther hills. He would be looking for a break, a pass, through which they could make their way. And always, when they reached a far rim of hills, there *was* a pass. The little band would climb up and over it and into another long, low valley.

As they traveled south they left the high peaks of the Rockies. The land was low and flat. The heat grew worse and worse. The trees and grassy meadows disappeared. Barren rock and scorching desert took their place. Water holes and springs were far apart.

The game disappeared. There was nothing, not even small rabbits, for the hunters to bring in. The men grew gaunt and weary. The horses and mules died. Jed ordered that each animal be skinned and cooked.

The men began to grumble. "Where does Old Jed think he is taking us?" they whispered among themselves. They called him "Old" because he knew so much and was so keen, although he was only twenty-seven. "There's nothing down here. It's time we turned back."

Old Jed said nothing. With his eyes on the horizon, he moved steadily on. He seemed always interested and excited, no matter how little there was to see. And each night, beside the campfire, he wrote in his little book. Then he read his Bible aloud to those who wished to listen.

Here and there the little band came across small parties of Indians. Jed, always somewhat ahead of his men, would approach these with his hand raised in friendly greeting. And always the Indians would respond in friendliness. The Sampatch Indians gave him rabbits and flint arrowheads. The Paiutes presented him with a marble pipe. The Mohaves, in their green valley on the Colorado River, fed the men with green garden beans and luscious ripe melons.

Jed let his men rest here among the friendly Mohaves. For two weeks they slept and ate and drank to their hearts content. Then, with Indian guides, they turned west.

Before them lay the white-hot sands of the Mohave Desert.

"I thought we'd been through fiery furnaces,"

one of the men grumbled, "but this is worse 'n anything I ever did see."

"We ought to turn back!" muttered others. But they knew they could not turn back. And they knew that Jed Smith would not turn back, even if he could. The search for beaver, the desire to explore led him on and on. He knew now what belonged in some of that blank space on his old map, but not in all of it. He must go on where Americans had never gone before.

Day after scorching day passed. The men grew gaunt again. There were long, torturing stretches between water holes. Often, just as the men felt they must die of thirst, Jed would point forward.

"Just a little way farther, men!" he would urge. "There's water ahead." And when they had gone just a little farther, there, true enough, would be water. The men looked at their captain. They began to think there was some sort of magic in him. They followed him, grumbling and muttering, hungry and thirsty, but sure that he would get them through.

For fifteen desperate days the weary little party made its way across this barren desert. And then, one morning, they saw far ahead of them the shimmering, cool blue of a mountain range. They threw themselves down on the blistering sand. Rough as they were, they felt like offering a prayer of thanksgiving.

They reached the foot of the blue-colored mountain range. Jed, with his knack for discovering mountain passes, led them up and up. There were trees here, and grass, and, best of all, water. They made camp.

Jed studied the pass. It had been traveled, but not often. He called Abraham LaPlant, the interpreter, who had journeyed farther than the others into this region.

"Just a little farther, men!"

"Where are we?" he asked. "Who goes over this trail?"

Abraham shrugged. "Not many. This is the Cajon Pass. Over this mountain lies California. There are farms and the missions from Mexico. Sometimes the Indians run away from the missions. They come over this pass, seeking escape. And from this side, sometimes, Indians slip over

Jed urged. "There's water ahead."

to steal the excellent horses from the Spanish."

"White men?" Jed asked. "Do they come this way?"

Manuel Lazarus, another member of the party, said, "I believe not. I believe no white man has ever crossed this mountain."

The listening men saw a strange light in their captain's eyes. He turned his head and stared upward.

The next afternoon the men saw their captain pause in his upward climb. He had reached the top of the pass. He stood there above them, outlined against the bright afternoon sun. They hurried to his side. Their eyes followed his. Below them lay green fields and well-kept farms. Behind them towered the mountain peaks. On one the men saw a giant arrowhead marked in the glistening snow.

But Jed was not looking at these things. His raised hand shaded his eyes from the setting sun.

He was staring far, far out. And there, beneath the sun, lay a shimmering band of blue.

"The Pacific!" Jed whispered.

The men yanked off their tattered caps. They threw them in the air. They shouted with joy. "The Pacific! The Pacific!" . . . "Old Jed brought us through!" . . . "Hooray!"

Jed turned his gaze away from the ocean. He looked northward and stared at peak after peak of towering mountains. "I wonder what lies there," he muttered.

"We don't care what's up there, Cap'n! We're in California now. That's enough for us!"

Jed was still looking north at the mountains. Now he answered his men. "We'll rest awhile in California," he promised. "And then we must go on. There is still much to be seen and learned."

"Gar!" grumbled Silas Gobel, the blacksmith. "He'll never rest. Them moccasins of his will never be still so long as there's a new trail to follow."

Jed heard Silas. He smiled. "Come along, men!" he said. "Let's go on down."

The men followed their captain down into the green valley.

XII

GREAT RANGES OF THE WEST

1. *A Map Is Drawn*

ALL St. Louis was agog with excitement. A huge crowd had gathered at the big fur barn down near the wharf.

"Greatest caravan ever to come out of the mountings!" one old fellow said enviously. "And wagons too!"

"Never thought it could be done, no sirree!" another said. "Why, only five years ago, the Mountain Men were a-saying that no wagons could ever be dragged across the Stonies!"

"They've even changed the name of those mountains!" a third watcher put in. "Call 'em Rockies now. Gar! Look at the peltries!"

The men crowded closer. Before them were huge stacks of furs—beaver, mostly. But also there were heaps of buffalo robes, packs of mink and otter and muskrat.

"General Ashley sure's a smart feller!"

"Ashley! He didn't do this! It's that young fellow—Jed Smith, and his pardners. They went up into the mountains seven or eight years ago. Now they've come out rich as kings."

"Yep! They say those furs are worth a hundred thousand dollars if they're worth a penny."

"It's a mighty good thing for this-here town, too. If it weren't for the fur trade St. Louis would go to the dogs!"

The talk and the confusion down at the wharf did not reach the ears of the men who were being talked about. Jed Smith, and his partners, Davy Jackson and Bill Sublette, were reporting to one of the most important men in St. Louis. General Ashley had used all the money he got from the fur trade to good advantage. He was important in both the politics and the business of the growing city.

"See, General," Jed said. He opened his buckskin pouch. "See what I've brought back in my possibles bag." Jed smiled at the word. He remembered what one of the Mountain Men had told him: "They call it a 'possibles' bag because it holds everything possible, so you can do everything possible, in every possible situation."

General Ashley leaned over the table on which Jed was emptying his treasures. "Here's some salt I collected from the shores of Salt Lake. Look at it, sir! Better than the finest Liverpool salt!"

General Ashley moistened his finger and dipped it into the glistening crystals. Then he tasted the salt. "Mmmm. It *is* good," he said. "What do you have to do to make it so white and pure?"

"Nothing! Just scoop it up. There are miles of it! And here's another kind of salt. We got this down near the Mohaves."

General Ashley touched the tip of his tongue

to the pinkish rocklike lump. "That's good salt, too!"

"And here's a pipe the Paiute Indians gave me. It's made of a very fine pink pipestone. They have a mountain of it. And this is the kind of plant that grows in the deserts—all prickly. But it has beautiful flowers on it in the springtime."

One by one Jed took out the things he had collected and saved to bring back and show the American people. He wanted them to know what the West was really like.

"And what are you going to do now, Jed?" his friend asked.

Jed's gray eyes shone with excitement. "I'm going to write that atlas! Years ago, Dr. Simons, my old teacher, and I planned this—now I can do it!" He thought for a moment. "Can you tell me who is a good map maker? I must have my maps absolutely right!"

General Ashley knew everyone in St. Louis.

He told Jed, "Get young Parkman to help you. He's interested in the West, and he can draw maps."

So it was that Jed stood, one cold day in November in the year 1830, among a small group of interested workers. They were in the study of the new home he had bought in St. Louis. His partners were there. There were his brothers Peter and Ira. And there was young Sammy Parkman. They all leaned across the big round table on which lay the parchment and the ink for the maps.

"Now, about that lake—what did you call it, Mr. Smith?"

"We all call it the Salt Lake," Jed answered. "Draw it like this sketch."

"How did you ever find out its shape?" Parkman asked curiously.

"Four of my men traveled all the way around it in a bullboat. That's a tub-shaped boat made out of skins." Jed smiled. "It was a long, hard trip, but they described it very well when they got back. They told me where the lake shore goes north, where west, where the bays are. Put them in as I've drawn them, Sam."

2. *The Last Journey*

Day after day through the winter Jed and his friends worked on the map and the atlas. And they worked on Jed's book which was to tell all about his experiences. They worked all through the short days and the long evenings. But when the days began to get longer and the warm sun called them out of doors, Jed set aside his writing for a while. His fiddle-feet began to itch for the long trail. A faraway tune began to hum in his ears again.

And so early in April he and his brothers and his friends set out for one more adventure. They would take a caravan of goods to the rich Mexican market at Santa Fe.

Because Jed's moccasins had grown restless,

Jed was attacked by a band of Comanches.

the atlas and the book were never finished. On the way to Santa Fe, Jed was attacked at a water hole by a band of Comanches. He had ridden ahead alone, looking for water for his company. Though he fought bravely, he could not defeat the whole band. He never returned to his home in St. Louis and to the atlas he had hoped to give the world.

3. *They Followed the Pathfinder*

Though he died there in the desert on May 27, 1831, Jed's work as a pathfinder and an explorer was not lost. People all over the country heard about the South Pass in Wyoming Jed had discovered. They heard how he had taken a caravan of wagons and carriages through the Rocky Mountains—the first man to do that—and that he was the first man to go from the Missouri River overland to California.

Jedediah Smith

And he had been the first to travel by land up the coast of California and Oregon. He had ranged over the West from the Missouri to the Pacific, from Mexico to Canada. He had seen more of the Indians than any other man.

People learned about the atlas he had started and the maps he had drawn. They learned from him so much about the West that many of them decided to go out past the Rocky Mountains to find new homes for themselves. "We can take wagons now!" they said. "We can take our families! No use letting the Mountain Men have all that country to themselves!"

And so the wagons set out—at first just a few. But in less than twenty years after Jed began his map, thousands of white-topped wagons were moving slowly and steadily across the Plains, over the South Pass, into the Oregon Country— or into Utah Territory—or on into the rich gold fields of California.

2989